3   D0898183

INDIANS

POCAHONTAS, *Seymour*
SACAGAWEA, *Seymour*
SEQUOYAH, *Snow*
SITTING BULL, *Stevenson*
SQUANTO, *Stevenson*
TECUMSEH, *Stevenson*

NAVAL HEROES

DAVID FARRAGUT, *Long*
GEORGE DEWEY, *Long*
JOHN PAUL JONES, *Snow*
MATTHEW CALBRAITH PERRY, *Scharbach*
OLIVER HAZARD PERRY, *Long*
RAPHAEL SEMMES, *Snow*
STEPHEN DECATUR, *Smith*

NOTED WIVES and MOTHERS

ABIGAIL ADAMS, *Wagoner*
DOLLY MADISON, *Monsell*
JESSIE FREMONT, *Wagoner*
MARTHA WASHINGTON, *Wagoner*
MARY TODD LINCOLN, *Wilkie*
NANCY HANKS, *Stevenson*
RACHEL JACKSON, *Govan*

SCIENTISTS and INVENTORS

ALBERT EINSTEIN, *Hammontree*
ALECK BELL, *Widdemer*
CYRUS McCORMICK, *Dobler*
ELI WHITNEY, *Snow*
ELIAS HOWE, *Corcoran*
ELIZABETH BLACKWELL, *Henry*
GEORGE CARVER, *Stevenson*
GEORGE EASTMAN, *Henry*
HENRY FORD, *Aird and Ruddiman*
JOHN AUDUBON, *Mason*
LUTHER BURBANK, *Burt*
MARIA MITCHELL, *Melin*
ROBERT FULTON, *Henry*
SAMUEL MORSE, *Snow*
TOM EDISON, *Guthridge*
WALTER REED, *Higgins*
WILBUR AND ORVILLE WRIGHT, *Stevenson*
WILL AND CHARLIE MAYO, *Hammontree*

SOCIAL and CIVIC LEADERS

BETSY ROSS, *Weil*
BOOKER T. WASHINGTON, *Stevenson*
CLARA BARTON, *Stevenson*
DAN BEARD, *Mason*
FRANCES WILLARD, *Mason*
JANE ADDAMS, *Wagoner*
J. STERLING MORTON, *Moore*
JULIA WARD HOWE, *Wagoner*
JULIETTE LOW, *Higgins*
LILIUOKALANI, *Newman*
LUCRETIA MOTT, *Burnett*
MOLLY PITCHER, *Stevenson*
OLIVER WENDELL HOLMES, JR., *Dunham*
SUSAN ANTHONY, *Monsell*

SOLDIERS

ANTHONY WAYNE, *Stevenson*
BEDFORD FORREST, *Parks*
DAN MORGAN, *Bryant*
ETHAN ALLEN, *Winders*
FRANCIS MARION, *Steele*
ISRAEL PUTNAM, *Stevenson*
JEB STUART, *Winders*
NATHANAEL GREENE, *Peckham*
ROBERT E. LEE, *Monsell*
SAM HOUSTON, *Stevenson*
TOM JACKSON, *Monsell*
U. S. GRANT, *Stevenson*
WILLIAM HENRY HARRISON, *Peckham*
ZACK TAYLOR, *Wilkie*

STATESMEN

ABE LINCOLN, *Stevenson*
ANDY JACKSON, *Stevenson*
DAN WEBSTER, *Smith*
FRANKLIN ROOSEVELT, *Weil*
HENRY CLAY, *Monsell*
JAMES MONROE, *Widdemer*
JEFF DAVIS, *de Grummond and Delaune*
JOHN MARSHALL, *Monsell*
TEDDY ROOSEVELT, *Parks*
WOODROW WILSON, *Monsell*

Henry Clay

Young Kentucky Orator

Illustrated by Gray Morrow

Henry Clay

Young Kentucky Orator

By Helen Albee Monsell

THE **BOBBS-MERRILL** COMPANY, INC.
A SUBSIDIARY OF HOWARD W. SAMS & CO., INC.
Publishers · INDIANAPOLIS · NEW YORK

To Lucile
Daughter of the South

Illustrations

Numerous smaller illustrations

Contents

★   ★

Books by Helen Albee Monsell

Henry Clay

Young Kentucky Orator

The Baptizing

HENRY CLAY was nearly four years old. On this particular day he was very much excited.

The year 1780 was an exciting time in Hanover County, Virginia. The Revolutionary War had been going on for nearly five years. Many people were discouraged. They were worried and excited too over the news.

"The British have taken Georgia. They have taken South Carolina. Soon they will reach Virginia. They will burn our homes."

But Henry wasn't excited about the war. He was very sure that if soldiers ever came to burn his home, Father would drive them away.

It wasn't the war that was worrying him. No, indeed. This was something really important.

"Please," he begged. "Please."

"He isn't four years old yet," said Mother, "but he's big for his age."

"I am bigger than any of your other children were when they were four," boasted Henry. He drew himself up so that Mother could see how very big he was.

Mother laughed. "You are certainly big enough to know how to behave."

"Yes, ma'am."

"What do you think about it, Father?"

"Well, a preacher should start taking his children to meeting while they are young."

"That's true."

"And I would like to have him see a baptizing."

"All right, then."

Henry ran outdoors before they could change their minds.

There were two little Negro boys in the yard. They were bringing a bucket of water from the springhouse to the kitchen.

"Jim!" called Henry. "Little Sam! I'm going to the baptizing with Father tomorrow!"

The boys put their bucket down in the path.

"You'll have to get up mighty early," said Little Sam. "It's a right smart way to the river."

"You won't get back for dinner," warned Jim.

"I don't care. Someone will ask us to dinner. They always ask the preacher. It will be company dinner, too."

Little Sam smacked his lips. "Company dinner is mighty grand."

But Jim shook his head. "No such a thing. The trouble with company dinner is that there's always too much company. The company eats all the chicken legs. It eats all the white meat. By the time the children get called to the second table, there's nothing left but wings and necks."

13

Old India came to the kitchen door. India was the cook. When she called a little Negro boy, he had to hustle.

"You, Little Sam, Jim, where's that water?"

"We're a-coming." They picked up the bucket together and started for the kitchen.

NOT ALWAYS SAFE

Henry wakened early the next morning. The roosters were crowing. A blue jay outside his window was making a great fuss.

But Henry did not have time to listen. I haven't time to eat breakfast," he told Mother.

"It's going to be a long while before dinner," Mother reminded him.

Father took plenty of time. He took a second helping of corn bread. Then he took more bacon. But at last he said, "You may tell Aaron I'm ready now." Aaron was the coachman.

14

Aaron brought the horse and chaise around to the door. The chaise was a small carriage. It looked almost like a chair swung between two big wheels. Father was a big man. There was hardly room for Henry to squeeze in too.

They crossed the creek at the foot of the hill. They drove through the pinewoods. Goldenrod was beginning to bloom. Thistle pods were turning white.

Father slapped the reins over the horse's back. He looked down at Henry.

"Did you know that you once had a brother who was named Henry?"

Henry shook his head. How could his brother have his name?

"He died before you were born. We loved him so much that we named you for him. You must do all the fine things that he hoped to do."

"Yes, sir," said Henry. But he wasn't sure what Father was talking about.

Father drove for a little while without talking. Then he said, "When your brother Henry was a little boy, he never attended a baptism. I didn't dare take him."

"Why not?"

"It wasn't safe."

"Were there Indians?"

Father shook his head. "Sometimes I felt that it was worse than Indians. Indians are savages. You couldn't expect them to know any better. But these were white men. Sometimes they were our own neighbors. They felt that there is only one way to worship God. And that must be their way. They put our Baptist preachers in prison. They tried to break up our meetings. Once I saw some men throwing a big hornets' nest into a meetinghouse right in the middle of the preacher's sermon to drive the people out."

Henry remembered the time a hornet had stung him. He didn't like to think about it.

16

"They don't do that now, do they?" he asked anxiously. "They won't break up our meeting!"

"No. Americans are fighting for freedom. They want to be free to govern themselves in their own way. But they have learned that isn't enough. To be really free, people must be able to worship God in their own way too. Thomas Jefferson believes that. So does Patrick Henry. And they have helped get other folks to believe it. Nowadays no one tries to keep the Baptists from preaching."

"Oh!" Henry was certainly glad. "Besides," he told himself, "I reckon it's too late for hornets."

A FINE BAPTIZING

There were ever so many people on the banks of the river. Women and children were sitting on the big rocks. Men were standing beneath the trees along the river.

Father spoke to a large motherly-looking woman. She was sitting on a big rock. Two boys were with her. They were only a little older than Henry. The three boys stared at each other.

"Good morning, Mrs. Brown. This is my son Henry. May he stay with you during the baptizing? I think he'll be quiet."

"Of course," said the woman. "Come sit right here, sonny." She made a place for him by her side on the big rock. It was a very hard rock. Henry hoped Father wouldn't preach a long sermon before the baptizing.

Another rock jutted out into the river. Father used that for his pulpit.

First the people sang a hymn. Henry did not know the words but he sang as loud as anybody.

Then Father began to preach. Mother had said that Henry must stay quiet as a mouse. He tried his best. But the rock grew harder and harder. He had to twist and squirm just a little.

"Be still," whispered the big woman. She put her arm around him. She drew him close. Henry felt too warm sitting close to her, but she was soft. He began to drowse. He was nearly asleep. Suddenly he felt that something had happened. He sat up abruptly and looked about.

Father had stopped talking. He had come down from the rock. Now he was wading out into the river. Henry was excited.

An old man was the first to be baptized. Father took him by the hand. He led him out where the water was waist-deep.

"I baptize thee, my brother, in the name of the Father, Son and Holy Ghost."

He dipped the old man down in the river. The people on the bank sang another hymn. It was very solemn and very beautiful.

The old man came back to the bank of the river. The people shook hands with him. "Bless the Lord! Glory to God!" they said.

His wife had a coat to throw over his dripping clothes. They got into their wagon and drove away. They looked happy.

Next a young girl was baptized. Then came two men, and after them, a woman. There was a long line of people waiting to be baptized.

20

Henry wasn't sleepy now. He watched and watched. Finally the last convert was baptized. Father came up from the water. His clothes were dripping, too. He looked very tired but he looked very happy.

"It was a fine baptizing, Brother Clay."

"Yes," agreed Father. "The Lord has been good to us. Let us return thanks to Him."

A Hungry Boy

ALL THROUGH the woods now people were getting into their wagons and carriages. They were untying their horses.

"You and Henry must come home with me," Mrs. Brown told Father. "It's just a short way. You can get into dry clothes there. And, of course, you must stay for dinner."

"Company dinner," thought Henry. He wriggled with excitement.

Mrs. Brown lived near the river. Her home wasn't as big as Henry's, but she had more children than Henry's mother, and they seemed to be of all ages. Henry's mother had eight.

Some of Mrs. Brown's children were nearly grown. The baby wasn't old enough to walk. There were big girls and little girls. There were big boys, and there were the two boys, David and Frank, who were only a little older than Henry.

Henry had plenty of brothers and sisters to play with at home. There were also the little Negro boys. But he had met only a few other children. He felt shy with all these strangers. Besides, it was Sunday. They couldn't play anything, and they didn't know what to do.

"We can go look at the new colt," said David Brown. They went down to the barn.

Henry was beginning to feel that it had been a long time since breakfast. He wished he had eaten more corn bread and bacon the way Father had. He grew hungrier every minute. Why hadn't he listened to his mother?

"Isn't it nearly dinnertime?" he asked.

"It's nearly dinnertime for the grown folks," said David. "But Mother asked lots of people home to dinner today. There won't be room for children at the table. We shall have to wait for the second table."

"I wouldn't care," said Frank Brown, "if they would just eat as fast as they could and then get up from the table. That's what they want children to do. But grown people just sit and talk and talk. We shall have to wait and wait."

"Well, let's go see what Miranda is cooking for dinner anyway."

ONLY ONE PLACE

The kitchen was in a little house back of the big house. Fine dinner smells were coming from its open door. Henry sniffed eagerly. He thought he had never been so hungry. The children hesitated near the kitchen door.

24

"Miranda is mighty cross if we get in the way while she is toting the dishes across to the Big House. But she can't fuss if we keep out from under foot."

"Look! Here comes Cissy."

A little girl came running across the yard. "I've been counting," she said. "There's going to be one extra place at the table. One child can eat at the first table."

"It'll be Lydia," said David. "She's almost grown up anyway."

"Henry is the preacher's son and he is company," said Frank. "It will probably be Henry."

Henry hoped it would be. The chicken smelled so good he couldn't bear to wait and wait.

"Henry is mighty young to eat dinner with the grown folks," said David. "He probably wouldn't know how to behave."

"I do so. I mustn't ask for things or even speak. I must put my knife just so on the plate."

"Here comes Mother," interrupted Cissy.

"There's one place left at the table," said Mrs. Brown. "I believe Henry——" She stopped short. A man was riding up to the gate. He was leaning down to raise the bar.

"Oh, dear," said Cissy. "Here comes more company. Now it'll be so much longer before any of us children get anything to eat."

"I'm ashamed of you," said Mother. "That's no way to talk about guests. You must always be glad to see them."

She didn't say anything more to Henry about the first table. She hurried back into the house.

"Poor Henry," said Cissy.

"I don't care," said Henry. He did care, though. He knew he was too old to cry, but he certainly wanted to.

He must have looked the way he felt. Miranda was on her way back to the kitchen. She saw his face and felt sorry for him.

"Here, you children," she said. "You wait a minute, an' I'll bring you something."

She went back to the kitchen fireplace. She bent over the ashes. When she came back, she held four big baked sweet potatoes in her apron. "You just take these potatoes and wait." The potatoes were hot. Sweet sticky juice was oozing through their skins.

"Sweet potatoes aren't fried chicken," said Cissy, "but they're good just the same."

Cissy was big sister to the little boys. She liked to preach to them. "Now you look at Henry. He wanted to be at first table with the grown folks mighty bad. He didn't make a fuss, though, when he was disappointed. And now he's got something pretty near as good. You remember that too, Henry Clay. Don't you ever make a fuss when you can't get what you want."

Henry didn't answer. He was too busy with his sweet potato. He just looked up and grinned.

British Soldiers

For months after the baptizing Henry talked about it. All that winter and the next spring he tried to tell the people at home what had happened. He had been greatly impressed.

But Mother just said, "Yes, child." Henry knew what that meant. She really wasn't paying any attention. She was too busy thinking about something else.

His little brother Porter was too young to listen. His big sisters were too busy. His big brothers had something else to do.

Jim and Little Sam listened, though. "Land's sake! You must have had a fine time."

One morning in the late spring Mother came to the door while they were talking.

"You mustn't make such a noise. Your Father is sick today. Why don't you go play farther away from the house?"

"Yes, ma'am."

"Let's go down by the creek," said Little Sam. "We won't bother anybody down there." They went out of the yard and down by the creek.

"Machump's Creek," said Jim. "That's a funny name. It sounds like a great big old bullfrog."

"Father says Machump was a big Indian. He was one of Pocahontas' uncles. The governor invited him to dinner once. And he went to England too. He was a very important Indian."

"Humph, I bet the folks over there were surprised to see an old Indian walking down the street. I'll bet they stared at him."

"I bet old Machump was surprised at all he saw too. Think of an Indian going to England."

30

"Let's play Indians!"

But Henry was looking at the creek. "No, let's play baptizing."

Little Sam stuck his foot down in the water and drew it back.

"Water's mighty cold this morning. Who's going to do the baptizing?"

"I'll be the preacher, and I'll baptize you."

Little Sam shook his head. "Don't you go to baptizing me," he said. "I'll be one of the folks what stand on the bank and shake hands with the people when they come out of the water."

A spotted dog came down the path.

"We can baptize Spot! Here, Spot!" But Spot didn't want to be baptized either. He was too busy hunting rabbits. He pulled away from the boys and ran off into the woods.

"Catch him!"

Just then Aaron came riding down the lane. His horse splashed into the creek.

"Where are you going, Aaron?"

"Over to Hanover Court House on an errand for your ma."

Henry forgot about the baptizing. "Take me with you!"

"If'n your ma'll let you go."

Henry ran back to the Big House. "Mother, may I go with Aaron?"

Polly came to the door. Polly was Mother's maid. "Didn't your ma tell you not to make such a fuss? You just leave your ma alone and go on out and play."

"But I want to go to the Court House with Aaron. Please ask Mother if I can go. I won't get too tired."

"Well, I reckon you can go. It will keep you out from under foot."

He ran back down to where Aaron was waiting. He climbed up in front of Aaron. Off they jogged over the dusty clay road.

32

It was a long ride to Hanover Court House. Henry was asking questions the whole way.

"Look, Aaron. Yonder goes a rabbit. Why does a rabbit have a short tail and a squirrel a long one? Aaron, what makes the sky blue? Why can't dogs climb trees the way cats do? Why . . .?"

"You're the beatin'est boy for questions," said poor Aaron. "Now I'll ask you one. Why don't you ask something I can answer?"

Hanover Court House was a very little town. On one side of the road was a tavern. It stood back from the road in a green yard.

Aaron tied the horse to the branch of a tree which hung over the wall of the courthouse green. He helped Henry down.

"Now you play here in the shade while I do my errands. Don't you go where I can't find you. You mustn't get lost."

"Look, Aaron. Why are there so many horses hitched in front of the courthouse?"

"I don't know. 'Tisn't court day. But I reckon folks just come to find out the news. What with these Britishers rampaging around, folks want to know what's happening."

Aaron went to the back door of the tavern across the street. Henry played about under the tree for a while. Then he climbed up on the brick wall. From there it was easy to crawl out on the lowest branch of the tree. He rode it up and down. Swish! Swish! "This is the way I chase the British!"

He rode his horse so fast and so hard that it almost made him dizzy. At last he dropped off, down into the tall weeds inside of the wall.

This would be a good place to hide. "Only maybe Aaron would forget he brought me and go home without me. Maybe I had better get back in front and keep near the horse."

The gate was close by, but it was more fun to climb over the wall. The horse pulled back, startled, when Henry dropped almost under his nose.

"You didn't mean to step on me, but you almost did," Henry scolded. "It wasn't your fault, though. I was to blame for scaring you."

He went across the road for some tall grass and brought it back to the horse. Then he lay down in the shade of the tree. He watched some big black ants crawling up the trunk. Sometimes they were hidden by the bark. Where were they going? They couldn't keep on going up all the time. Where were they coming down? Maybe, if he looked over on the other side of the tree——

But the June sun was warm. He decided he would just stay where he was for a while. The sun was shining down between the leaves of the big tree, overhead. He closed his eyes to shut out the glare. Before he even realized he was sleepy, he was asleep.

The little town was very quiet. It seemed to be asleep, too. Even the chickens in the middle of the road huddled deep down in the dust and were quiet. For a while nothing disturbed them.

Suddenly a man on horseback came dashing down the road where the chickens were sleeping.

"The British are coming!" he cried. "The British are coming!"

The little town became alive in a second. The chickens flew squawking away from the horse's hoofs. Somewhere a woman screamed. The door of the tavern burst open. Men came dashing out. They raced for their horses. The horses snorted and plunged as the men mounted them.

The first shout had waked Henry. He saw Aaron come running across the road. Henry had never seen Aaron move so fast.

"Come along, child, let me lift you up on this horse. We're getting out of here quick. I hope we make it!"

Aaron dug his heels into the horses's side. As they galloped off, Henry looked back. Already he could see soldiers at the far end of the town.

A NEW GAME

After a long time Aaron slowed his horse down.

"I reckon we are safe now."

If Aaron wasn't afraid any longer, Henry wasn't either. He began to laugh.

"What are you laughing at, child?"

"It was so funny the way everyone began running and rushing all at once."

"Humph! If those British soldiers had caught you it wouldn't have been funny. I've heard tell they eat little boys for breakfast."

"Oh, Aaron! I don't believe that."

"Well, maybe they do and maybe they don't, but I'm going to steer clear of them, and you steer clear of them too."

They turned from the road into the lane. Little Sam and Jim saw them coming and ran to meet Henry. Aaron let Henry down after they crossed the creek.

"Are we going to play baptizing some more?" the boys asked.

"No," said Henry. "Now we are going to play 'The British are coming.'"

War

THEY were still busy playing when old India rang the bell for dinner. "I'll come right back," Henry told Jim and Little Sam, "as soon as dinner is over."

But he didn't. When he went into the house, he found his sister Molly crying.

"What's the matter?" he asked.

"Father is very ill."

Mother didn't come to dinner at all. She was taking care of Father. Brother George was nearly fourteen now. He tried to carve the roast the way Father did. Sister Sally poured the milk instead of Mother. But nobody ate much.

After dinner Henry didn't feel like playing. Aaron had gone to get Aunt Mary, Mother's older sister.

"Everything will be all right after Aunt Mary gets here," Henry told little Porter. But it wasn't. By the time Aunt Mary came, Father was very ill indeed. Soon after that he died.

NO LONGER A GAME

While Father was ill, Henry had forgotten all about the war. He had forgotten about the soldiers at the Court House. So had Mother.

The morning after Father was buried, Aunt Mary and all the other people who had come to the funeral went home. There was only one man left. He would help Mother run the farm.

Mother stood on the porch talking to him. Henry and Porter were sitting on the steps. Suddenly Little Sam came running down the lane.

"The British are a-comin'!" he called.

Henry thought Sam wanted him to play soldiers again. "I don't feel like playing today," he said with a yawn.

"I'm not a-playing, either. I mean it. They're a-coming. I went down the road a piece to see if any blackberries were ready to eat, and I saw them. I reckon there are 'most forty million of them, and they are headed straight for this house. Look a-yonder!"

The house was on a small hill. Henry and his mother could see a cloud of dust far down where the road curved.

"Maybe it's just more company," said Henry. "Horses always raise a lot of dust."

"It's soldiers, I tell you!"

If they caught the new overseer, they would take him prisoner.

"Slip out the back door and go hide in the woods," Mother told him.

"But that would leave you with no one to protect you!" protested the overseer.

"One man couldn't help against all those soldiers. Go quickly or it will be too late."

42

The overseer hurried down the wide hall. He went out the back door. He escaped into the woods. He would be safe there. Already the soldiers were splashing across the creek. Then the whole yard was filled with them. They jumped down from their horses. The chickens began to squawk. Dogs barked. One of the children screamed and the others whimpered.

"Be still!" said Mother.

The soldiers made for the kitchen. They swarmed into the storehouse and the smokehouse. They looked in every cupboard.

"They want food," said Mother.

There was plenty of food. People had come from miles away to Father's funeral. There had been a good dinner. Ever so much was left.

Soon the soldiers had their mouths and their hands full. They brought out hams from the smokehouse. They brought bags of flour and corn meal from the storehouse.

Henry watched them fasten these supplies on the backs of the horses. They were taking all the food the Clay family had.

"They mustn't take our things," cried Henry.

"They need supplies," said Mother. "This is war. Soldiers take the supplies they need."

After the soldiers got the food they needed, they went through the rest of the house to see what else they could find. Some of them wanted presents to send to their families at home. Some of them broke things up just for the fun of breaking them.

"This is war!" said Mother again, but her eyes were beginning to sparkle. Henry knew what that meant. Mother wasn't frightened. She was getting angry.

Henry went upstairs. He kept out of the way but he had to see what the soldiers were doing. Some of them were chopping open a chest where Mother kept all her finest linens.

"Maybe there's some jewelry in here."

One of them kicked down the door to the cupboard where the feather beds were stored. Mother had a cool straw mattress for each bed in the summer and warm feather beds for the winter. The feather beds had just been put away.

"Hey!" called the soldier. "They may have hidden some money in these beds."

He dragged a feather bed to the window and ripped it open with his sword. Other men pulled out the other beds. The air was filled with feathers. It looked like a snowstorm. It would take weeks to clean up the lawn.

Then the soldiers broke open the bureau drawers. They began to rummage through Mother's clothes. They threw her things about the room and stepped on them with their dirty boots. They took what they wanted. Henry couldn't bear it any longer. He ran downstairs again to find his mother.

45

Some men were searching through Father's desk. They were saying rude things to Mother. Mother's eyes were sparkling more than ever. When she looked like that, her children always stepped lively.

She stood by the window and looked out. The soldiers were all over the yard now. Father's grave was in the little cemetery lot just beyond the garden. One of the soldiers saw it.

"Maybe they've hidden their money there!" he cried. Several ran toward the grave. They crowded around it.

Mother could stand no more. "Stop!" she cried. Just then the officer in charge rode up to the porch. He jumped from his horse and strode into the hall. Mother turned on him. She told him what his men had done. Then she told him exactly what she thought of him and his men.

"Show me which of my men were rude to you," he said.

"You know I can't do that. They were all shouting at once. They were all over the house, and they all looked alike to me."

"Then at least, madam, I can pay you for your losses. I apologize for their behavior." He emptied a small sack of coins on the hall table and quickly left the house.

The soldiers were getting ready to leave now. Henry watched them catching chickens and turkeys to carry off. The men laughed and shouted whenever they caught another one of these big birds. They even took the pet rooster, which always followed Henry about the yard.

One of the men came from the house. He was carrying Mother's wedding dress. He threw it across the saddle on his horse. Then Mother broke down and cried.

The soldiers rode away. Some of them were shouting. They dashed down the hill. They were gone almost as suddenly as they had come.

47

"Oh, dear!" said Mother. "Oh, dear!"

She looked at the lawn covered with feathers. The porch and the hall were marked with muddy boot tracks. The papers from Father's desk were scattered all over the room. Two of her best chairs were broken. She stopped crying. Her eyes flashed again.

"Polly!" she called. "Get another one of the girls and let's start cleaning this room."

"There isn't any use in calling the servants," said Sally. "They ran away when they saw the soldiers coming. They hadn't any guns, of course. They are hiding out in the woods."

"I'm glad they are," said John. "If they had tried to hide in the house, they would have been caught. What would we do without them?"

"That's right," George agreed. "Every cupboard in the house was broken open."

"Here they come," cried Sally.

Sure enough, India, Polly, and the maids were coming up the path from the springhouse down by the woods. They looked like scared rabbits. When Spot jumped at them, they started to run back to the woods again.

"You're safe now," George called. "The soldiers have gone."

"Come on," said Mother. "Let's get to work. Polly, build a fire in the fireplace. India, bring a mop and some buckets. George, you and John go see what damage has been done outside. You younger children clear out from under foot."

Soon everybody was busy, but Mother was still angry. She came to the table where the officer had tossed his money. Her eyes snapped.

"Does he think I'd take money for the things they stole? That would be selling my goods to the enemy. Besides, no amount of money could pay for my loss. Why, I wouldn't even soil my fingers with his money!"

She used the hem of her apron so that she wouldn't have to touch the coins. She brushed them into her apron. Then she threw them into the fire.

Little Sam and Jim had hidden in the woods too. After the soldiers left, they had gone down to the servants' quarters. Now they came running up the path.

"Hey!" they called. "The British have carried off the field hands. How are we going to run this farm without men to work in the fields? We can't raise our crops!"

"We'll all starve!" wailed Jim.

Henry looked at Mother. Mother wouldn't let them starve. Her lips looked like a straight line. But she didn't look frightened.

"No," said Mother, "we won't starve. But we'll all have to work. You boys go down to the springhouse and fetch me another bucket of water. We'll begin working right now."

Working for Their Food

MOTHER WAS right. They didn't starve. But everybody had to work.

Henry had always taken what he had to eat for granted. Mother would open the pantry and the storehouse every day to give India what she needed. India would cook it. Then the big bell was rung. The bell called, "Time to eat!"

Now it wasn't that easy at all. Henry began to understand that they must grow corn before they could have meal. They must raise pigs before they could have ham. Aunt Mary lent them some servants to work in the fields, but there were many other things that had to be done.

Henry had to help, too. He could pick up apples. He could go with his mother to feed the chickens. He could carry messages.

He often wished he could have been the youngest or the oldest of Mother's children, instead of in the middle.

"Everybody thinks I am too old to be babied any longer," he told Little Sam. "That's right, I am. But they think I am too young to do the things the big boys do. That's not so, but Mother and the boys think so. It isn't fair."

"What do you want to do so much?"

"I want to have a knife, for one thing. A good knife—that really cuts."

"You'd more'n likely cut yourself."

"No I wouldn't either."

But there was no use to argue about it, because he didn't have the knife. He knew Mother wouldn't get him one, even if he were old enough. Good knives cost money.

There was no harm in talking about it, though. "If I just had that knife," he would tell Little Sam, "I could cut me a whistle down in the swamp. I could make stick soldiers."

He was so busy talking about it that he didn't even notice when Mr. Henry Watkins rode into the yard. Mr. Henry Watkins' brother was Aunt Mary's husband. Both of them often rode over to see how Mother was getting along, and to advise her about the work on the farm. Today he didn't get down from his horse. He asked Little Sam to run tell Mrs. Clay that he was on his way to Richmond.

"I'll be gone for several days. Ask her if I can do any errands for her down there."

Little Sam ran to call Mrs. Clay. Mr. Watkins looked down at Henry. "What is all this about a knife?" he asked.

Henry felt suddenly shy. He dug his bare toes down into the dust.

54

"I want one," he said at last.

"Every boy does, I reckon," said Mr. Watkins. "Why can't you have one?"

"They say I'm too little. That's silly."

"I'm not sure about that. A boy who doesn't know how to handle a knife can do a great deal of damage with it."

"I do know how. I wouldn't cut anything Mother didn't want me to, and I wouldn't hurt myself, either. I'd be careful."

Mr. Watkins smiled. "Would you promise me that?" he asked.

"Of course I'd promise."

"Well——" said Mr. Watkins. "Well——"

Just then Mother came to the door. She and Mr. Watkins began to talk about other things. When Mr. Watkins rode away he didn't say another word about knives.

"What do you suppose he meant by 'Well ——'?" Henry asked Little Sam.

"It's hard to tell what grown people mean when they talk," Little Sam told him, "unless they say 'Don't!' or 'Stop!' or something like that. Sometimes they don't seem to mean much of anything."

"You're right."

Three days later Mr. Watkins came back. He stopped to give Mother the package of things she had asked him to buy. Henry stood watching. First he stood on one foot and then on the other. He knew he mustn't ask Mr. Watkins. Children must not ask for things. But just suppose Mr. Watkins had bought a knife in Richmond and then forgot all about it. Henry wanted to remind him.

"Well," said Mr. Watkins at last, "I'd better be getting along." He mounted his horse.

Then, just as he was turning, he put his hand down in his pocket. "Oh," he said, "here is a package from Richmond for Henry."

56

Henry didn't need to open the package to find what was in it. He knew.

"A knife!" he cried. "Little Sam! Jim! Come see my knife. I've got my own knife!" He started to dash across the yard.

"Henry!" Mother called sternly. "Come back here. Where are your manners?"

Henry came back sheepishly. "I'm sorry, Mr. Watkins," he said. "I forgot." He made a funny little bow. "Thank you, Mr. Watkins."

Then he turned and ran toward the back of the house again. Mother and Mr. Watkins looked at each other. Both of them laughed.

It wasn't only to Little Sam and Jim that Henry showed his knife. He showed it to every one in the house. He showed it to all the relatives that came to visit. He showed everyone how sharp it was.

"Mr. Watkins," he said, "is the very nicest man I know."

"That isn't saying so much," teased Molly. "You don't know very many men because you live away out here in the country."

"I do so, too. I've been to the courthouse lots of times, and I know the innkeeper and the men in Father's church and——"

"Come, come," said Mother briskly. "There is work to be done. Henry, come carry my basket down to the henhouse for me. You can help me gather the eggs. We mustn't waste our time."

But she wasn't scolding. She was smiling.

"Why," thought Henry, "I believe she likes to have me like Mr. Henry Watkins."

Soldiers

THERE WERE days when Henry would forget all about the war. The older boys would be too busy to ride over to the courthouse for news. There were very few visitors to tell them where Cornwallis and Tarleton were or what they were doing. Sometimes, for two or three weeks, they would hear nothing at all.

Then in the middle of a busy morning Little Sam or Jim would come running across the fields.

"The British are coming! I saw them down at the forks!"

Everyone would stop work in a hurry. There would be a bustling and a scurrying.

Mother had a box for the little silver that was left. "Help me with this box. Hurry!" They would carry it down to the garden. They would bury it in a hole under one of the rosebushes.

Out in the kitchen India would rush around.

"There aren't any thieves and robbers what can catch old India napping a second time. They've taken Missus' hams already. But they aren't a-going to get the bacon and side meat. Hey! You Jim and Little Sam, you get busy."

They would carry what was left of the meat down into the woods and hide it in a hollow tree.

But the British never came to the farm again. Maybe they knew they had already taken practically everything. Maybe they were sorry for the Widow Clay and her children.

When word came that the soldiers had gone on, Mother would dig up her silver. India would send the boys out to bring back the meat, and everyone would go on working.

But sometimes is was a different story. "There are some of our own men down in the woods."

Then Mother would fix up a big basket of supplies. There would be bread and some of the precious meat. There would be roasting ears from the garden. Aaron would pack the food in saddlebags on a horse. Then Mother and Aaron would take it to the soldiers.

Once Little Sam came running in. "The Frenchmen are going by."

All the children went dashing down to the road. They wanted to see the brave men who had come across the ocean to help the Americans. They climbed up on the fence. They waved at the French soldiers who were marching past.

"Hurrah!" the children cried. "Hurrah!"

Some of the men looked very tired, and their uniforms were stained and dusty. One of them smiled at Henry. "My own leetle boy, he is just about so big as you."

It was very hot that summer. It seemed to Henry as if he could hardly remember the last time it had rained. The roads were thick with dust. It rose in clouds whenever a wagon went by. It settled on the grass, weeds, and crops.

"How we need rain!" worried Mother.

"And we're gwine to git it. I feel it in my bones," Polly answered.

Sure enough, that night Henry waked suddenly. The wind was blowing. Polly came running in to close the windows. The rain was dashing against them.

"You go back to sleep. 'Tain't nothing but a quick shower."

But she was wrong. The next morning it was still raining—and the next. There wasn't any dust now. The road was so thick with mud that it was hard for even a man on horseback to ride along. No one tried to travel in a wagon.

"Huh! said Polly. "We wait and wait for rain, and now it's come, it won't stop!"

When George came in to dinner, he was wet through and through. He was mad through and through too.

"Someone has stolen my biggest watermelon. I brought it up from the field just before the rain began. I put it in the creek to get cool and now it's gone."

"Maybe some soldiers stole it," said Jim.

"More likely it was one of you boys. Look here! Did you steal my watermelon?"

"No, suh!" Jim backed away. "I didn't steal a thing! No, suh!"

"Well, I'd just like to get my hands on the rascal who took it."

After dinner Little Sam called Henry to one side. "You know, I don't believe anybody stole that watermelon. The creek's been rising and the watermelon floated off."

"It's a mighty big melon," said Henry.

"Yes, suh! And it's a mighty big creek right now. It's rampaging along something terrible."

"Well, the melon is gone, anyway."

"Maybe it's floated plumb down to the river. But then again maybe it's got caught in the bushes some place. If we should find it, I reckon that melon would belong to us, wouldn't it? Let's look for it!"

Henry wasn't sure. "But I reckon George would give us a good big piece of it, anyway."

He slipped out the back door when Polly wasn't looking. He joined Little Sam down by the springhouse. They started down the creek. The rain was letting up now. It was only a drizzle. Henry could hardly feel it in the thick woods, although his clothes were damp.

But the wet ground was like a sponge under his bare feet. Whenever he ducked under the low branches of a tree, he got a fresh shower.

He had never seen the creek look like this before. Last week he had waded across it. To-day not even a man could get across. He couldn't even see the banks. The water covered the bushes on each side. The trees stood deep in water. There were plenty of places where a watermelon could get caught.

This was farther down the creek than he had ever been before. The woods were very thick.

"Yonder's a clearing," said Little Sam.

"And I hear someone talking," said Henry.

"Maybe it's Britishers. Us had better go back."

"Maybe they're eating George's watermelon. Let's get close enough to see."

The men weren't British. They were American soldiers. They were standing on a high place on the other side of the creek.

"Hello!" they called.

"Hello!" called Henry. "Have you seen our watermelon?"

The men laughed. "No, indeed. We surely would like to see it—or anything else to eat. How long will it take this creek to go down so we can get across?"

"Quite a while," shouted Little Sam.

"We were afraid so. Well, it won't be the first time we've gone without our dinner in Washington's army."

"But we've never slept on wetter ground," said another man.

"You wait," Henry called. "I'll tell Mother."

The men laughed. "I don't believe your mother can do anything about it, sonny."

But Henry knew that Mother could always do something about things. He was right, too. Mother didn't even seem surprised.

"There are scouts and pickets all over the countryside now," she said. "Polly, will you go tell India to fix up a basket of hard things—apples and potatoes—things like that?

"Little Sam, go call Aaron for me."

"Aaron can't get across that creek any more than the soldiers can."

"That's all right. He'll know what to do."

Aaron picked up the basket.

"Now Henry, you and Little Sam will show him where to go."

Aaron grumbled when they led him through the wet bushes.

"My rheumatiz is sure going to kill me tomorrow. But I'm not so old but what I've still got a good arm."

The soldiers were surprised to see Henry come back. They were glad to see Aaron with the basket too.

"How can we get it across the creek?" they called. "We can't come after it!"

"Don't you fret," Aaron shouted back. "Can you catch what I throw? That's all I want to know."

He stood close to the water's edge. He took an apple from the basket. He threw it as far and as hard as he could.

"Caught!" cried the soldier.

It was a strange game of ball. Henry handed the things from the basket to Aaron. Aaron threw as hard as he could. Sometimes the soldiers missed. Then the food fell with a splash into the muddy water. But they caught enough to keep them from going hungry.

"Thank your mother for us," they called to Henry. "Thank her ever so much. We don't suppose that you could throw us a nice dry bed now. We're standing in the mud here."

"Go back up in the woods a piece," called Aaron. "You'll find some big rocks there. There's a hollow place underneath. 'Tisn't a cave exactly, but I reckon it's drier than outside."

He picked up the empty basket. "My rheumatiz has caught up with me already."

He grumbled all the way home. Henry didn't pay much attention. He had started looking for the watermelon again.

Almost back at the house he found it. It had been carried by the water only a little way. It was caught by the bushes. He could just see its smooth, round top.

"I found it! I found it!" cried Henry. "It's mine now, isn't it, Aaron, because I found it?"

"Well, I don't rightly know," said Aaron. "It was your brother's melon all right. But you found it all right too. I reckon your ma will have to decide."

When they got to the house, Mother and George were waiting for them. George looked pleased when he saw the watermelon. He reached out to take it.

"Oh, that's mine," he said. "Where did you find it? Give it over."

70

"But I found it. It belongs to me now, doesn't it, Mother?"

Mother thought for a moment. "You were going to share it with us, weren't you, George?"

"Yes, ma'am."

"You would share it with us too, wouldn't you, Henry?"

"Of course."

"Well, then, if we're going to share it, what difference does it make who owns it?"

The boys grinned. "It doesn't make any difference," said Henry. "Let's eat it right now."

Soap Making

"I THINK fall is the best time in the year," said Sally. "It's warm enough to be comfortable outdoors. It's cool enough for a fire inside. I like a nice, jolly fire."

"That's because you don't have to tote the wood," grumbled Aaron. He had just come with an armful of wood.

"It's beautiful too," insisted Sally. "Look at those gorgeous sweet gum trees."

"I'd rather look at that hickory-nut tree," George said. "The nuts are beginning to fall now. You youngsters had better start picking them up."

"It's not the best time in the year to make soap," said Mother, "but the British ruined a large part of what I made last spring. We'll need more before the winter is out."

"It doesn't matter if you make soap in the spring or in the fall," Aaron told her, "just so long as you don't make it in the dark of the moon. But if the moon's not right, you don't get any soap at all."

Mother laughed. "Will the moon be all right tomorrow? I'd hate to have us do all that work without getting any soap."

"Yes'm. There'll be full moon now in just two or three nights."

"Good! Then ask India if the leach barrels are ready."

Henry didn't think much of soapmaking. Old India was always cross then. She didn't have time to fix him any snacks, and she was always telling him to keep out from under foot.

73

"Let's go play down by the creek," said Jim the next morning. That's so far off nobody can hear when she calls me and Little Sam to get wood. She'll keep us a-humping if we stay around where she can call us."

But even if Henry didn't like soapmaking, he wanted to watch.

"All right! All right!" Jim said. "You can go ahead and watch. "We're going persimmon-hunting. Stay here if you want to."

Henry stayed around and watched. For weeks India had been saving every scrap of fat. She had saved wood ashes from the fireplace. Now she put the ashes in a barrel. She poured water over them. The water trickled through the ashes. It dripped through a hole in the bottom of the barrel into a wooden tub. This was the "lye."

Mother watched everything carefully. "I don't believe that lye is strong enough, India. You had better pour it over some fresh ashes."

At last the lye was strong enough. When Mother dropped a potato in, it bobbed around.

Then India built a fire in the yard. She hung a big kettle over it. She poured the grease and lye into the kettle. She stirred it with a big stick. It looked a mess. But India worked over it patiently. The grease disappeared. A clear soft jelly began to form. This was the soft soap.

It took a long time. Henry grew tired of watching. Besides, India needed more wood.

"Where have those two rascals gone?" she grumbled. "Just wait till I get my hands on them."

Henry decided maybe he had better get out of sight too. He ran around to the front of the house. He wondered which way the boys had gone. He looked down the lane toward the road.

"Mother!" he called. "Company is coming. I see someone on horseback. He is turning in from the road. And he's in a mighty big hurry."

Mother came around to the porch. "So he is!" she exclaimed. She shaded her eyes with her hand. "I do believe it is Mr. Henry Watkins. I hope nothing is wrong at Sister Mary's!"

"I'll go open the gate," said Henry.

But the two boys down in the woods had seen Mr. Watkins too. They got to the gate first. They had it open so that he could ride through.

"Big news!" he called as he jumped from his horse. "Word has just come to Hanover Court House. Cornwallis has surrendered!"

Mother sank down in a chair. "May God be praised!" she said. It was as if she were saying a prayer in church. The girls had come running from inside the house.

"Does that mean the war is over?" asked Sally.

"Well, yes and no. Of course, peace hasn't been declared yet. But there'll not be much more fighting, I expect."

"And I was almost big enough to be a drummer boy," Henry said. "Why couldn't it have lasted a little longer?"

They all laughed. Then Mr. Watkins looked at Henry and became serious.

"Don't you fret, sonny. You may be too young to help make our country free. But you will have to help keep it free when you grow up. That isn't any fun. It isn't even exciting. It's just hard work. It's worth while, though."

"Yes, sir," said Henry. But he didn't quite understand what Mr. Watkins meant. He still wished he might have been a drummer boy.

Off to Kentucky

THE WAR for Independence had begun before Henry was born. He could hardly realize that now, at last, it was over.

It was good not to have to worry any more about the British coming. Mother could keep what silver was left on the sideboard again. The cows could be driven down to the creek pasture. The hams were safe in the smokehouse.

Soldiers still went along the road every now and then, but they were on their way home.

"I should think they would hate to have to take off their uniforms and become just plain farmers again," said Henry.

Mother shook her head. "Fighting isn't fun. Any soldier will tell you that. Most of them will be mighty glad to get back home in time to start their spring plowing."

Henry looked up at the big oak tree in the yard.

"Aaron says that when the new oak leaves are the size of squirrels' ears, it's time to plow."

"It is as good a time as any, I reckon." Mother looked anxiously down the lane. "I do wish your Aunt Mary would come a-visiting. It has been weeks and weeks since I have seen her."

Henry knew that during the winter it was almost impossible to drive over the rough roads. When the deep ruts were frozen they could turn a carriage over easily. When they melted, the mud was so thick that even strong horses could hardly pull a carriage through.

Today the air was warm. The spring breeze was drying the mud.

80

"I expect Aunt Mary will get here almost any day now," he said happily.

ANOTHER NEW GAME

Springtime was good for something else, too. It was the time for a new game. When Little Sam said, "Come on, let's play soldier today," Henry shook his head.

"We'll play a new way. We'll make rules."

"That is just an old game. We used to play that even before we played baptizing."

"But we'll play it a new way. This time we are going to have rules."

The new way was fun. Soon the other boys on the farm were playing it with them. They were having such a good time they didn't even notice a big carriage coming down the road. Aunt Mary was on her way to spend the day with Mother. Cousin Betsy was with her.

The carriage had almost reached the big gate. There was a field on one side of the road. It had just been ploughed. There were thick woods on the other side. The branches of a big tree hung over the road. Suddenly a boy dropped from the lowest branch. He plopped right in front of the carriage. Betsy gave a little scream.

"It's Henry!"

The coachman stopped the horses.

"Don't you know you must never jump in front of horses that way?" asked Aunt Mary. "You'll get run over. I declare, it's a wonder boys ever live to grow up. They do such foolish things. Girls have more sense."

"You'll make the horses run away and kill all of us," said Betsy.

Henry dug his toes into the dirt. He looked so unhappy and embarrassed that Aunt Mary was sorry she had scolded him.

"Get in and ride up to the house," she invited.

Henry shook his head. "I can't, 'cause I'm not a white boy right now. I'm a red Indian."

"Oh," said Betsy. "That's why you have those feathers in your hair."

He nodded. "It's a game. Little Sam and Jim and I are Indians. John and his boys are settlers. They want to take our hunting grounds away from us. We Indians hide in the woods. Then the settlers have to get from the springhouse to the big oak tree down by the road. If they can get there before we catch them, they can be the Indians. But if we catch them, we scalp them. Then they have to start all over again."

"It sounds like an exciting game."

"Yes, ma'am. We catch them and scalp them 'most every time. We call the game 'Going to Kentucky.'"

"Oh, don't call it that," said Betsy.

"But that sure enough happens when you go to Kentucky. There are Indians and bears and——"

"Don't," begged Betsy.

"Why not?"

"Because we are going to Kentucky. That's what we have come to tell your mother about."

AUNT MARY'S PLANS

Henry left the other boys to play "Going to Kentucky" without him. He wanted to hear everything Aunt Mary could tell about this big new adventure.

Mother was almost as excited as he was. "But I'm not surprised," she said. "Mr. Henry Watkins told me you had just about made up your minds to go. When will you leave?"

"Just as soon as we can. We had to wait until spring so the roads would be fit for travel. But we have to hurry. We must get through in time to plant our crops."

"Will you go by way of the Ohio River?"

Aunt Mary shook her head. "They say the Indians are pretty dangerous along that route. We will go through Virginia and across the mountains."

"That road is hard and dangerous, too."

"Oh, I despise Indians," broke in Betsy.

"It isn't only the Indians that make travel bad. Outlaw white men hide in the mountains."

"My husband says that we can make it," insisted Aunt Mary. "Other people do. More and more families are moving out there every day."

"I know," said Mother. "Taxes are high here. And so much of our land is worn out from raising tobacco. You can get rich land out in Kentucky and get it cheap, too. Then you can leave a good farm to each of your children. I almost wish I were going there with you."

Henry didn't "almost wish" it. He wished it very much! He wanted to see the mountains. He wanted to hunt bears and fight Indians.

"Maybe you'll all come join us some day. I declare, I hate to leave you here with no one to take care of you."

"Mr. Henry Watkins will take care of us," said Henry. "He comes to see us often anyway."

Aunt Mary looked at Mother. She suspected that his frequent visits meant something.

"Yes." Mother smiled. "Mr. Henry Watkins will take care of us."

"Good! Then I won't worry about you here alone with the children."

THE SALE

Mother and Mr. Henry Watkins were married before Aunt Mary left for Kentucky. Mr. Watkins came to live at the Clay farm. He ran the farm for mother. Henry liked Mr. Watkins. And Mr. Watkins liked his new family. They got along together very well.

They all hated to see Aunt Mary leave. And it took a lot of work to get her ready to go.

Just before she left, there was a big sale at her house. Mother went over to help her. She took Henry and Porter along. "But you must keep out of the way of the grownups," she said.

The house looked funny. Furniture was piled out in the yard. The things Aunt Mary was going to take with her were packed up in one room.

"Your house looks like ours did when Tarleton's men had been through it," Henry told Betsy. "There aren't many of your nice things left here."

"It certainly doesn't feel like home any more," Betsy said gloomily.

"Don't you fret," said Aunt Mary briskly. "We'll have a nice new home out in Kentucky in less than no time."

"But it'll be only a log cabin."

"Maybe so, just at first. But it will be home."

After the sale Aunt Mary and her family went home with Henry and Porter and Mother to spend the night. The next morning they started for Kentucky.

Mother stood on the porch as the wagons drove away.

"Good-by!" she called. "Be sure to send me a letter as soon as you can."

"I shall. But it may be weeks before I can find someone coming back this way who can bring it. Don't worry about us."

Henry and the boys had run down to the big gate to open it. They climbed up on the fence and waved.

"Good-by! Don't let the Indians catch you!"

"And don't forget," called Aunt Mary, "some day you are coming out to Kentucky too."

"No, ma'am," shouted Henry. "I shan't forget. I hope we'll see you soon."

88

The Ha'nt Hunt

"Look," said Little Sam to Henry, "do you believe in ha'nts?"

"Of course not," said Henry. "Well, I don't believe in them in the daytime, anyway."

"But this one is a daytime ha'nt."

"It can't be."

"But 'tis. I went fishing with Jim yesterday, way down the creek. There were footprints in the mud. Don't any humans ever go down that way. It must have been a ha'nt."

"Where did the footprints go to?"

"Good lands! We didn't wait to find out. We weren't aiming to go ha'nt hunting."

"Mother says there aren't any such things as ghosts, or ha'nts, or anything like that."

"You can come look at the footprints your own self."

"All right," said Henry, "I will."

"It's a right smart way from here. You'd better ask India to fix us up a good-sized snack."

Henry went out to the kitchen. He asked India to fix them a good-sized snack.

India was in a good humor. She got some fried chicken from the pantry. She cut some cold light bread. She broke open some biscuits. She put thick slices of ham in between. She tied it all up in an old napkin. "There!" she said. "Now I reckon you won't starve."

Henry thanked her. Then he and the boys started down the creek. The woods were thick and green. So were the brier patches. It was good that Henry's trousers were made of thick homespun cloth. It would take tough briers to tear them. The breeze couldn't get in under the thick trees. The air was hot and close.

"It's a long way," said Henry.

"Yes sir-ee! All the way to where we found those soldiers once."

There had been no rain for a long time. The creek wasn't roaring now. It was so small that Henry could wade across.

At last they came to a place where the woods thinned out. There was a big patch of blackberry bushes.

"Look a-yonder!" cried Jim.

Down by the creek bank there were footprints. They were big footprints too.

"Now do you believe in ha'nts?" asked Little Sam. "Even in the daytime?"

"Let's see where the footprints go," said Henry. "Come on. We'll follow them."

The footprints came up from the bank. They went to the blackberry bushes.

"There," said Henry, "you see, it was just one of the field hands. He was after some blackberries. He knew the biggest and the best ones grew down here."

"All the field hands are working over in the south field today. And your pa has got them a-humping themselves to get the corn hoed. They haven't got any time to come way down here for blackberries."

Henry knew that was true. "But maybe they came yesterday."

"These footprints aren't all the way dry yet."

That was true, too.

"Well, anyway," said Henry, "ha'nts couldn't eat blackberries. So it isn't a ha'nt."

"You're right." Jim sounded relieved. "Ha'nts wouldn't have any use for blackberries."

But Little Sam wasn't sure. "If 'tisn't a ha'nt, where did these footprints come from, and where do they go? How come they start and stop right here?"

"The man must have waded up the creek," Henry decided. "Let's wade down. Maybe we can find some footprints on the other side."

They waded down the creek. Sure enough, they soon found footprints on the other side.

"What did I tell you?" asked Henry.

"Where did they come from?" insisted Little Sam. "You tell me that!"

They followed the footprints back from the bank. At last they came to some rocks. There the tracks disappeared.

"You see! Not even an Indian could follow tracks over bare rocks."

"Listen!" said Jim.

A strange noise was coming from somewhere in the rocks. It sounded half like a groan and half like a teakettle boiling over.

Jim began to get frightened again. Even Henry didn't feel quite as brave as he had been before. He had never heard a noise like that.

But Little Sam grinned. "My grandad makes a noise like that when he snores."

"Oh!" said Henry. Then he remembered something. "Aaron told the soldiers there was a sort of cave here in the rocks. I reckon one of the field hands is in there taking a nap. We'd better wake him up and send him back to work before he gets caught."

They followed the noise back through the rocks. Sure enough, they found a hollow place almost like a cave. And there lay a big Negro sound asleep.

"But he isn't one of our boys," whispered Henry. "I've never seen him before."

"No," Jim agreed, "we never saw him before."

Just then a big fly buzzed over the man's head. It settled on his nose. He slapped at it and waked with a start. He saw the three boys looking at him, but he didn't give them any time to be frightened. He was too frightened himself.

"Please, please!" he begged Henry, "don't you go tell anybody I'm here. Please!"

"Where did you come from?" asked Jim.

"Who are you?" asked Little Sam.

"I'm Ike. I belong to folks across the river."

"You have run away?" asked Henry.

Ike nodded. "My master, he treated me something awful."

"Did he whip you?"

"He surely did. Look at my back. Please don't tell on me, where I am. He'll 'most kill me!"

"We won't. But you can't stay here forever."

"I'm waiting until the full moon has gone. When the nights get black, I can get away without anybody seeing me."

"Are you hungry?"

The man's eyes shone. "I sure am. Of course, I'm not starving exactly. I know where all the berry patches are. I catch fish. And when the frost comes, I can show you some fine fox grapes. But I'd like to put my teeth into some honest-to-goodness victuals."

Henry opened his snack.

"It seems like we have to feed somebody every time we come down here," grumbled Little Sam. He had wanted some of that ham himself. But even he didn't mind when he saw how hungry the man was.

Watching him made Henry hungry too. "We'll bring you some more dinner tomorrow," he promised. "But we'll have to go now. It's almost our own dinnertime."

HUNGRY BOYS

The next morning Henry went out to see India again. This time she wasn't in a good humor at all. She shooed him out of the kitchen as if he were a bothersome fly.

"I haven't got any time to be fixing snacks. You boys think I can spend all my time waiting on you. You clear out of here."

"We'll have to wait and go after dinner," Henry told the boys. "Each of you save all the dinner you can without getting caught."

"Henry must be hungry," his sister Molly told Mother at dinner. "That's his sixth biscuit."

"They're good," said Henry. He hoped she wouldn't notice that he wasn't eating them. He was stuffing them into his shirt. He took a big piece of ham when nobody was looking. He hoped it wouldn't make a greasy spot.

Little Sam and Jim came up to the Big House after their dinner. Little Sam had a piece of corn bread. Jim had a potato. They hurried down to the woods.

The runaway was glad to see them. "It gets mighty lonesome down here," he said. "I'll be glad when it's time to travel."

So would the boys. Feeding him became harder every day. At last the full moon was gone. The nights grew dark.

"I reckon I'll set out tonight," the Negro said. "I'll head toward the North. I'll never forget you boys. I'm mighty thankful for what you-all have done for me. God bless you!"

THE NOTICE ON THE DOOR

Mr. Watkins was riding over to Hanover Court House the next day. "Would you like to come along?" he asked Henry.

Of course Henry wanted to go along. First they went to the courthouse, where Mr. Watkins attended to some business affairs. Then Mr. Watkins went to the inn across the road. Henry waited for him by the door.

There were only two or three newspapers in Virginia. People had to have some other way to publish notices. Sometimes they would take them to the nearest innkeeper. He would tack them on his door.

Mother had been teaching Henry to read. He tried to read the notices on the door of the inn while he was waiting for Mr. Watkins. There was a notice about a lost cow. There was a notice about a new doctor. There was a notice about a runaway slave.

Henry was excited. That must be his runaway slave. Henry was glad the man had got away.

Mr. Watkins and the innkeeper came to the door. They saw Henry reading the notices.

"Here is one that needn't stay up any longer," said the innkeeper. He tore down the one about the slave.

"Has he been caught?" asked Mr. Watkins. Henry held his breath. He was sure it was the man he'd been helping to hide in the cave.

"He wasn't caught," said the innkeeper. "He was killed when they tried to take him."

Henry almost cried out. Maybe, after all, it wasn't his man. But it was.

"He belonged to a fellow across the river," said the innkeeper. "Folks say he'd been treated very badly."

Mr. Watkins shook his head. "Slavery is bad enough with a good master. But with a bad one——"

"Well, in this case the bad master has lost a good slave. A strong fellow like that must have cost him at least sixty pounds."

"And it serves him right. Come along, Henry. We must be getting home."

MAKING UP HIS MIND

Henry was very quiet all the way home. That evening he sat by himself under the hickory tree. He thought about the man who had been killed. He thought for a long time.

Henry already had two slaves of his own. Father had left him Jim and Little Sam in his will. He knew that he would have many more when he grew up. Then and there he made up his mind he would always treat his slaves kindly. Then they wouldn't want to run away.

"Come, child," called Polly, "it's time for you to go to bed."

"All right," said Henry, and he came into the house. All the while he was undressing he kept on thinking. He was still thinking when he fell asleep.

"There must be some way. When I grow up, I will try to find it."

Ploughboy

TIME WENT by fast. Before Henry could get used to its being summer, it was fall. Then winter came. Then, almost before he knew it, spring and summer would be back again.

Polly said Henry changed as quickly as the weather did. "By the time I get a pair of britches made for that boy, he's grown big enough to split them! I could sew for him all the time."

Maybe time went so quickly because there was so much to do. It wasn't only Henry who kept busy. Everybody on the farm did.

"I declare," said Mr. Watkins one morning, "I just don't know what to do. I wanted to finish plowing the south field today. What with the wet weather, we're a week late, as it is. But I must go to see Mr. Page about some cattle. And every man on the place is busy."

"I'll plow it," said Henry.

Everybody laughed but Mr. Watkins. "It's not such a bad idea. You'll never start any younger, that's one thing certain. Besides, the whole place belongs to you boys. You might as well begin to learn to run it."

Henry felt very grown-up when he harnessed the mule. He slapped the reins over her back.

"Get up!" he cried.

Down at the field he hitched the mule to the plow. He picked up a handful of dirt as he had seen the men do. He pressed it into a ball. Then he threw it onto the ground. It broke and scattered when it fell. Yes, that meant it was just right for plowing. Now he would begin to take care of his own land and do it right.

He felt very grown up indeed. He grasped the handles of the plow. "Get up!" he called again to the mule.

But he hadn't known the plow would be so heavy. He hadn't known it would be so hard to manage. Sometimes he pointed it down too deep. Then the mule couldn't pull it. She would stop short. Sometimes he would point it too high. Then it would come right out of the ground. Sometimes it would hit a small rock and jerk almost out of his hands.

And he hadn't known how hard it was to plow straight! He stopped at the end of his first furrow and looked back. "A crow would get cross-eyed trying to find the corn in that furrow," he decided. "I must keep that plough straight."

The mule thought she knew a lot more about plowing than Henry did. The best thing about plowing, the mule thought, was to stop. She would stop often. Then Henry would have a

time getting her started again. He began to understand what Polly meant when she said that
he was "stubborn as a mule." He would have
to be even more stubborn than this mule if he
were to get the ploughing done.

Slowly, however, he learned how to handle the plow. He learned how to handle the mule. But his arms began to ache. So did his back. The sun grew hot. He was becoming tireder, hungrier, and thirstier every minute.

He was glad when his sister came down to the fence with a jug of cold water and some cakes India had just baked

He looked back at the furrows. "They are straighter now, don't you think?" he asked anxiously. "Don't these last ones look better?"

Molly thought they were very straight. And when Mr. Watkins looked at the field that afternoon, he said Henry had done a good day's work.

That made Henry quite proud of himself. But John laughed.

"You think yourself smart today, don't you? You'll be changing your mind about that pretty soon. Now you've proved you are big enough to work, you'll have to keep on working."

John was right. Tarleton's men had taken the best field hands away with them. There was no money to buy new ones. Grandfather had left the plantation half to Mother and half to Aunt Mary. Mother and Father had been buying Aunt Mary's half when Father died. Now Mother and Mr. Watkins were finishing the payments for the boys. It took all of their money. Until this was done, they couldn't buy new field hands.

So help was very short. The corn must be weeded. The wheat must be threshed. The small new shoots must be pulled from the tobacco plants. Everyone had to work hard.

But Henry didn't mind working. And not all of life was work. Now that he was old enough to work with them, John and George decided he was old enough to go around with them, too. Henry liked that. There came a time when the crop had been laid by.

They could go fishing. They could go swimming, too. Henry had learned how to swim in the creek. The water was shallow there. But the older boys didn't swim there.

"Let's go to the river," said George.

It was a long tramp. Most of the way was through the woods. The pine tags, the dried pine needles, were slippery under their feet.

At last they came to the Pamunkey River.

"There's a good swimming hole down on the other side of the road," said George.

It didn't take long to get out of their homespun shirts and trousers. Then they plunged in. The water was fine.

This swimming hole was much larger than the one in the creek. All the same, Henry swam across it four times without stopping. He was sure even the big boys could do no better.

After a while they grew tired of swimming. They lay on the bank and talked.

"I remember the first time I ever came to this swimming hole," said George. "It was the summer right after the war. I was with the Page boys. I got my clothes off first. I wanted to show off. So I jumped in.

" 'How deep is it out in the middle?' they called. 'Can we touch bottom?'

"I swam out to the middle and let my feet down. My feet touched something cold and slippery.

" 'Ouch!' I yelled.

" 'What's the matter?'

" 'There's something down there.'

" 'What is it?'

" 'I don't know. It isn't alive. It's too hard. But it's too round to be a rock.'

"The other boys plunged in. They felt around the thing. It was long and hard and round. What do you think it was?"

Henry couldn't guess.

110

"It was a cannon."

"Cannon? In the middle of the river?"

"Yes, sir! There were four or five cannons. You see, they were being brought to protect Hanover Court House during the war. But Cornwallis' men captured them on the way. They spiked them and rolled them into the river."

"Look!" said John, "we're only a couple of miles from the Court House now and it's court day. Let's go see what's going on."

The Orator

HENRY had never been to Hanover Court House with the boys before. It was very different from going with Mr. Watkins. Then he did what Mr. Watkins wanted to do. He stood around waiting while Mr. Watkins talked. He seldom had anything very interesting to do. Now he did what he wanted to do himself.

The little town was crowded on court day. Everybody knew that everybody else would be in town. They would come even if they had no business at court. They would come to meet their friends. They would come to do their trading. They would come to listen to the speeches.

112

Horses were tied to the hitching posts by the green. They were tied to swinging limbs of near-by trees. Some of them were munching at their oats. Some of them were swishing flies away with their tails. Even the horses seemed to enjoy court day. Perhaps they, too, liked a change.

"I've never seen so many horses," said Henry, "but not a man is in sight."

"That means everyone is inside the courthouse. Something special must be going on. Let's go see what's so exciting."

Sure enough, the courthouse was packed. Henry wasn't sure they would let boys in. But George was almost a man now. Besides, every-one was too busy listening to pay any attention to them. They squeezed in and stood against the back wall.

A man was standing there in front. He was speaking to the jury.

"It's Patrick Henry!" whispered George.

113

No wonder everybody crowded in to listen. Patrick Henry was one of the finest orators in all the country. Once he had been a boy here in Hanover County.

"Why," thought Henry, "he probably has been swimming in the very swimming hole I've just come from." And now he was one of the most famous men in America. He had been one of Virginia's leaders in the struggle for independence. He had been her first governor when she became a state.

Henry looked and looked. He listened and listened. He forgot the people around him.

After Patrick Henry's speech was over, the courthouse green seemed to come to life again. Men stood around in little groups talking. One group was arguing about the new Constitution. Over yonder a man was selling his horse. Some of the men had been drinking. Henry saw one or two fights.

"Well," said George, "it's about time for us to start home."

George and John had an argument of their own on the way home. Henry didn't even listen.

"Do you know what I'm going to do when I'm a man?" he asked. "I'm going to make speeches like Patrick Henry."

IT TAKES MORE THAN PRACTICE

Molly came to her mother the next day. She was laughing.

"I was down at the barn just now, hunting for eggs. I had climbed up on the hay. I heard the funniest sounds. So I looked down. And what do you suppose I saw? Henry was down there. He had got onto the back of an old wagon and he was making a speech to the horses and mules."

Mother laughed too. "He must have been playing he was Patrick Henry."

It was John who had the next story to tell.

"I was coming through the wood lot the other day. I heard a peculiar noise. I poked my head through the bushes. There was Henry standing on a rock. He was waving his hands and spouting away to the squirrels."

"You were playing Patrick Henry again, weren't you, son?" laughed Mother.

It seemed to Henry that Mother should know he was too old to play silly games now.

"I wasn't playing," he told her. "I was practicing. Mr. Patrick Henry most probably had to practice too when he was a boy."

"You just get up and talk," teased George. "Is it such hard work to be an orator?"

"It is, indeed. Somehow your voice doesn't do what you want it to do at all. You think it's going to sound a certain way and it doesn't. You have to try and try until you get it right. You have to practice all the time."

117

"Right you are!" agreed Mr. Watkins. "But it takes more than just practice to make a good orator. Something else is more important."

"What?" asked Henry.

"Well, you have to know what you are talking about, for one thing. And you must be sincere for another. You must believe in what you say."

Henry thought that over. "Why?" he asked.

"How can you expect to make other people believe you if you don't believe yourself?"

"Yes, sir. I see that."

"There is another reason. It gives you a fine feeling to be able to make folks think and do what you want them to do. But it also makes you responsible for what they think and do. Responsibility is a big word. It is a big burden to take on your shoulders. So you must be sure you really believe in what you are saying."

"But how can you always be sure?" asked Henry. "Mr. Madison says people should vote

118

for this new Constitution. Mr. Richard Henry Lee says they shouldn't. How can you be sure which is right?"

"You must learn to think things out for yourself. Then perhaps you may be able to explain them to other people."

"Oh," said Henry.

"It's hard," Mr. Watkins admitted.

"Yes, sir, but all the same, I am going to be an orator."

Mill Boy of the Slashes

"MR. WATKINS," said Mother one morning, "our corn meal is running mighty low."

"Corn meal must be mighty important," teased Mr. Watkins, "if you expect me to take a man from his work all day just to go to the mill."

"Well, if you want any corn pone or hoecake or egg bread or crackling bread or——"

"All right," laughed Mr. Watkins. "All right. Henry, you take the day off and go to the mill for your mother."

Henry grinned. He knew it was a long, dusty trip. Already the sun was hot. But he liked to go to the mill anyway.

Mr. Watkins threw a big bag of corn over the back of one of his mules. Henry used the bag for his saddle. He dug his bare heels into the mule's sides. He was off to the mill!

The countryside around Henry's home was low and swampy. Such land was called "slashes." The pine trees which grew in the swamps were called slash pines. Henry was glad there were so many of them. It was cooler in the pinewoods than out under the broiling sun. But the mosquitoes were bad.

Blackberries grew along the side of the road. The bushes were so high he could pick the berries without getting off the mule. He passed huckleberry patches too.

At last he came to the mill. It was built where the river bank was steep. Above the mill was a dam. It held the water back in a small pond.

There were several horses tied to the trees near the mill. Men and boys were sitting on the stone

steps and under the trees. They were waiting their turn for their meal to be ground.

This was the part about going to the mill that Henry liked best. He tied his mule to the low branch of an oak tree. He joined the boys over by the pond.

THE STORY OF PETER FRANCISCO

For a while the boys wrestled and scuffled with one another. They rolled over and over on the grass. But the day was too hot for much of that. Then they sat and listened to the men talking.

"Have you heard the latest story about Peter Francisco?" asked one.

Henry had seen Peter Francisco. Folks called him the "Giant of Virginia." He was six and a half feet tall. He weighed two hundred and sixty pounds by the time he was sixteen years old. This story was going to be good.

"A man rode up to Francisco's inn the other day," the man began.

" 'We've heard about you all the way out in Kentucky,' said the man, 'and I've come over the mountains just to show that here's one man strong enough to whip you.'

"Peter didn't want to fight. He called to his servant, 'Go get me a handful of switches down by the creek, please.'

"The boy brought back the switches. Peter handed them to the stranger.

" 'Switch me around the shoulders. Then you can go back home and tell your folks you have whipped Peter Francisco.'

"The fellow was sure he could lick anybody. He was vexed that Peter wouldn't fight.

" 'Let me feel your weight, anyway.'

"Peter was getting vexed too. He wanted to get rid of the stranger. He let the man lift him a little from the floor two or three times.

124

" 'You're sort of hefty, aren't you?' the fellow said. 'Bet you never found anybody else who could lift you.'

" 'Now let me lift you,' said Peter.

"He lifted him twice. The third time he tossed him over a four-foot fence. The man landed in the road."

Henry and the boys laughed aloud. Tossing a grown man over a four-foot fence!

"Wait a minute," said the storyteller. "That's not all. The fellow sat up in the road. He looked a little startled.

" 'Well,' he called, 'put my horse over after me and I'll go.'

"So Peter put one hand under the horse. He put the other hand on the horse's chest. He lifted the horse up. He put it down on the other side of the four-foot fence. He said the horse looked rather surprised. But the man looked even more surprised than the horse."

125

"Tell us some more stories about Peter Francisco," begged the boys.

But the men wanted to talk about more serious matters. The war was over now. Virginia and the other states were free. What kind of government should they have? What about this new Constitution? Was it good or bad? So far the thirteen states had been bound together only by an agreement called the Articles of Confederation. Should they really become one country—a "United States of America"?

"It's the only way that we can stay alive," insisted one man.

"We'll lose everything we have fought for," objected another.

"The President will soon become another king, just like King George."

"George Washington wants the Constitution."

"Patrick Henry doesn't."

126

They became excited. Henry thought once or twice there would be a fight. But finally the man who was against the Constitution got his corn meal and went away. The others stopped talking politics. They began to ask one another about their crops.

Henry and the boys weren't interested in crops. They went back to their own tree. They began to make up games.

"I bet I can whistle louder than any of you," said the oldest boy.

Each tried. Henry was the poorest of all.

"His mouth is too big," the oldest boy said.

"What can you do with such a big mouth?" asked the boy.

"I can grin," said Henry. "I bet I can grin wider than any of you." And he could.

Then they lay on their backs and began to talk. They talked about good places to swim. They told about the fast horses they had at home.

After that they looked at the big mill wheel. The millrace led the water from the millpond to the wheel. The water fell on the wheel and made it turn slowly.

"But the wheel turns up and down while the millstones lie flat. How can one of them turn the other? Let's ask the miller if we can go inside and see."

The other boys thought it was too hot to bother. But Henry wanted to see.

"You are John Clay's son," said the miller. "Well, I reckon any son of his would have sense enough not to get into mischief. Look around all you want to."

Henry went inside. He went upstairs and down. He saw how the big wheel made the millstone turn slowly.

The air was dusty with fine flour and meal. The miller's clothes and cap were covered with it. So were Henry's when he came out.

His corn meal was ready now. He loaded it on his mule and rode home.

The children laughed when they saw his flour-covered clothes.

"You look like a mill boy yourself," they said. "You are our Mill Boy of the Slashes."

Henry grinned. "I'd like to be a mill boy," he said. "It's interesting."

So the nickname began. It stayed with him for years and years after he was a man.

A Trip to Richmond

HENRY AND Porter were fishing. It had been a long, warm, lazy afternoon. Even the fish were too lazy to bite. It was good, though, just to stretch out on the bank under the trees and look up through the green branches at the blue, blue sky. The boys had worked hard most of the summer. It was pleasant to rest.

Sometimes Henry's thoughts were far away. Sometimes he was almost asleep.

Suddenly there was a jerk on his line. He sat up in a hurry. The next minute he had pulled out a fair-sized sunfish.

"How many have you got?" he asked Porter.

130

"Just three."

"Same here. Well, if we want India to cook them for our supper, I reckon we'd better be getting along toward home."

The path led through an old field. Grasshoppers were jumping high in the weeds on each side. The dust in the path sifted between Henry's bare toes. It felt soft and comfortable.

"Fall is almost here, though," he told Porter. "We'll have to wear shoes again soon."

Neither of the boys liked the idea. Besides, Henry knew that by next year he would be too old to go barefooted even in the summer.

As they came toward the house a little girl came running to meet them. Henry and Porter had little half-brothers and sisters now.

"Come as fast as you can!" the little girl called. "Mother has a letter from Aunt Mary."

To receive any letter was a big event. They would talk for days about this one.

Mother and Mr. Watkins were sitting in the big hall. She had just finished reading the letter.

"How are Aunt Mary and Betsy?"

"They are both very well."

"Where are they? What are they doing?"

"They have bought a home in Versailles. They have bought a farm out in the country, too. She says the soil is very rich."

"What else does Aunt Mary say?"

"She wants us to come out and join them."

"What?" Henry was startled.

"That is the way I felt at first, myself," Mr. Watkins said, laughing. Then he added more thoughtfully, "But maybe it isn't such a bad idea after all.

"Well, let's go," said Henry. "I can't think of anything that would be more exciting."

"I don't know," Mother began doubtfully.

"Do you really think moving to Kentucky is a good idea?" Henry asked Mr. Watkins.

132

"This isn't my farm, you know. It belongs to you boys. Maybe it would be a good plan for me to go out to Kentucky. As your aunt says, the land out there is rich and cheap. I could buy a farm of my own, so that I could leave it to my sons, the way your father left his to you."

Mother was looking thoughtful, too. "It would be good to be nearer Sister Mary again. I have missed her."

"I'd enjoy being with my brother," said Mr. Watkins. "He'd help us find good land, too."

They began to talk about the plans they would have to make. At first they said, "If we go to Kentucky." Then they said, "When we go to Kentucky." They were impatient to start.

"What do you boys want to do?" asked Mr. Watkins. One of you, though, should stay here and take care of this farm. You'll have to decide this question among yourselves."

"That suits me," said George.

"I want to go to Kentucky," Porter told him.

"I'll go too," said John. "I'd like to take a look at the other side of the mountains."

This left Henry. Henry was fourteen now. He must soon decide what he wanted to do when he was a man.

"It's still new country out there," said Mr. Watkins. "I doubt if we'd be near a school and you've had precious little schooling, I'm sorry to say. I certainly wish you had more."

"I've had three years," Henry reminded him.

"But only three months in each year. And it was a mighty poor school at that."

Henry agreed. "Those benches were as hard as logs. And they were too high."

"Of course they were," laughed John. "They were logs—sawed in half. And remember how dark the room was when it grew so cold that we had to close the door. The only lights came from the flames in the fireplace."

"I remember," said Henry. "And I remember the whippings the schoolmaster used to give me. He whipped me for what I did. He whipped me for what I didn't do. Once he whipped me so hard you could see the red marks for days."

"Well, we've learned to read and write, anyway. What more do we need to know?"

"And I got as far in my arithmetic book as 'Practice.' I went farther than most of the other pupils in the school."

"That's not far enough," Mr. Watkins insisted. "Maybe it would be a good idea for you to go down to Richmond. You could get a place to work there and you could study at the same time. There are going to be fine opportunities in this country for educated men."

"Where would he live?" asked Mother.

"I don't know, but I must be in Richmond next week. Henry can come with me and we'll look things over. Perhaps I can help him."

So Henry went down to Richmond the next week with Mr. Watkins.

"We'll go to the Capitol first," said Mr. Watkins. "The Assembly is sitting now. Our good neighbor, Mr. Thomas Tinsley, is there. Maybe he will know of some place for you."

They rode through the Capitol Square. It was filled with ruts and gullies. There were horses everywhere in the Square.

The Capitol was still very new. From the top of the hill they could look down across the river. They could see Mr. Mayo's new bridge. It was nearly four hundred yards long. It was the finest bridge Henry had ever seen. Some people said it was the finest bridge in all America.

"It's just like Hanover Court House on court day, only more exciting," Henry decided. "There are even more horses, more men, and more everything. I like it here."

136

The Assembly was meeting. Men were coming and going all the time. The doorman called Mr. Tinsley. He came out and talked with Mr. Watkins. While they talked Henry looked inside.

Mother had insisted that Henry wear his best clothes for the trip.

"I reckon some of these men didn't have their mothers around," Henry chuckled to himself. There were hardly any two dressed alike. Some had on boots. Some had leggings. Some had knee breeches. Some wore homespun. Some wore fine silk.

"You can't tell a man by his clothes," the old doorman said. "Don't forget that. There are men in this room who are the best statesmen in America. They don't all wear silk coats with lace on their ruffles, either."

Henry watched and listened. He was so interested he almost forgot why they had come. At last Mr. Watkins called him.

"Mr. Tinsley is going to take us to see his brother," Mr. Watkins said. "His brother is Clerk of the Chancery Court. He always has several boys and men working under him. There is a lot of copying to be done for a court, you know. And you write a good hand."

They went to the court room in the basement of the Capitol. Mr. Tinsley's brother was there. He was glad to see them. He would surely remember Henry the next time they needed a new boy. Just now there was no place for him.

Henry was disappointed. So was Mr. Watkins.

"Mr. Tinsley's office would be a fine place for you. You could learn a lot from the things you copied. You would have time to study. This new country will have a great need for men who understand law. Your mother would feel she was leaving you in good hands, too."

"He will keep me in mind." Henry tried to be cheerful. "He promised."

138

"Yes, and when a Tinsley promises anything, he means it. Our day is not wasted. Now let's go in Denny's Store here and buy something to take home to your mother."

Henry had never been in a big store like Mr. Denny's before. It almost took his breath away to look at the crowded shelves. Coats, caps, muffs, books, preserves, tea, hats, ink powder . . .

"I didn't know there were enough people in Virginia to buy all these things," he said.

"Yes, indeed," Mr. Denny laughed. "Business is always good when the Assembly is meeting. People from all over the state buy enough to last a year. Business is so brisk I could use another clerk if I could find one. You wouldn't know of a likely boy, would you, Mr. Watkins?"

"Well, now," said Mr. Watkins, "I might—not for good, but maybe until a place in the Chancery Court office opens up. How about it, Henry?"

"Yes sir! You know of one all right!"

Compromise

HENRY HAD known that the clerk of the court was a busy man. He must keep all the records. He must have copies made of everything. There was a great deal of work for him and his helpers to do.

But he had thought that clerks in a store would have an easy time of it. He had thought all they had to do was to show things to customers. He soon found out that he was mistaken. Store clerks led a busy life, too.

Mr. Denny lived upstairs over the store. The two clerks lived with him. Mr. Denny saw to it that they were up bright and early so that they

140

could open the store on time. Henry had always been up bright and early at home. But somehow in the city it was a good deal harder to wake up.

He missed being outdoors. It was hard to stay in the dark store when the sun was shining and the wind was blowing. He could stand at the door and hear the river rushing over the falls.

"This would be a grand day to be out in the woods," he said to the other clerk.

"Only if you were home you wouldn't be out in the woods. You'd be working, probably, in the fields. At least this isn't as hard work as plowing."

"I don't know about that. Lifting these heavy bolts of velvet and satins up and down from the shelves all day is plenty hard work too. I never knew there were so many kinds of goods to make clothes from—silk, satin, velvet, crinoline, muslin . . ."

The other clerk laughed. "I wouldn't mind that if only people would all pay the same kind of money for them. But what with Spanish money and Dutch money and receipts for tobacco instead of money—I do wish we Americans had some money of our own."

"We're going to have some," Henry reminded him. "The last Congress voted to make some American money."

"But it's taking a long time to get it ready."

Just then two ladies came into the store. They wore thick wooden clogs to keep their slippers from getting muddy when they crossed the street. The clogs clattered on the floor. The ladies wanted to see some satin quilted coats. They wanted ostrich feathers and colored kid gloves. One of them bought a book for her boy.

After they had gone, Henry stood by the door again. "Look," he called. "Yonder comes a whole fleet of mountain wagons."

"Talk about hard work! Those wagoners really know what the words mean. Driving a six-horse wagon all the way from the Blue Ridge Mountains isn't any joke. Some of them have been on the road for weeks."

"Look at the fellow with the bearskins thrown over his horses for blankets. He must have a whole wagonload of furs."

"They bring just about everything—furs, hemp, beeswax. One of them was in here last week with a bunch of dried rattlesnakes. He said you could make a broth with them that was fine for folks with a cough."

Henry made a face. "I'd rather keep my cough, thank you."

Not all of Mr. Denny's customers were ladies. Men came too. They looked at the beaver hats. They bought snuffboxes and stockings and knee buckles and powder for their hair.

They talked about Virginia politics. They talked about the new capital of the United States in Washington. They talked about the Revolution in France. At home Henry had paid attention only to the things that happened right around him. Now he grew interested in what was going on outside. He became anxious to learn not only about Virginia but about the United States and the whole world.

GETTING THINGS DONE

"Henry," said Mr. Denny, "I have a friend coming to see me. He and I have some business to go over. His two sons are with him. I want you to take them out and show them the city."

"Yes, sir," said Henry. It would be good to get outdoors on a fine day like this.

He started out with the two boys. Henry knew exactly where he wanted to go. He wanted to go up on Capitol Hill and listen to the speakers in the assembly. But he had to please the boys. Right away they began to quarrel.

"I want to go down to the river," said Tom. "I want to see the ships."

"Bother the ships!" said Dick. "I want to go up to the Capitol."

"I want to see the new canal they are building."

"I want to see the new statue of Washington."

Each was determined to have his own way. It looked as if there was going to be a fight. Time was going by. If they didn't make up their minds in a hurry, they wouldn't get anywhere.

"Look," said Henry, "why don't you compromise? Then both of you can get what you want."

"What's a compromise?" asked the boys.

"Each of you give in halfway. We'll divide the day in half. We'll take a quick look at the ships and the canal. Then we'll hurry to the Capitol. We'll stay there just a short while too."

"All right," the boys agreed.

Main Street in front of the store was hilly. It was also muddy.

"Come this way," Henry told the boys. "They have made a cinder and ashes path over the crossing. If you walk here you won't get your shoes muddy."

He started the boys across in front of him. They began to push and shove each other. Henry chuckled. It wasn't so long ago that he would have been pushing and shoving, too.

Then Dick slipped. His foot went over the edge of the cinder path, down into the mud. His heavy boot was covered with thick, sticky, clay.

"Now you've got yourself into a mess!" jeered his brother.

"You pushed me!"

"Don't worry." Henry hurried to interrupt the quarrel. "You can clean it off on the grass when we get down to the creek."

"The trouble with Richmond," growled Dick, "is that you have such *muddy* mud. Down home we have clean, sandy dirt."

146

Tom kept hurrying along. "The trouble with Richmond," he said, "is that it is nothing but hills. You always have to be climbing up or stumbling down. Now, at home, the land is flat. You know where you stand."

Henry hadn't been in Richmond very long, but he found that already he didn't like to have outsiders criticize it.

"It seems to me the river runs under some right steep bluffs down your way," he said, "and those bluffs aren't exactly sandy, either.

"Did you ever hear about the birds that build their nests in the side of the bluffs?" He made his voice sound serious.

"Do they, really?" asked Dick.

"They peck away at the side of the bluff all day trying to make a hole big enough for themselves and their eggs. Sometimes night catches up with them before they finish. What do you suppose they do then?"

"What?" the boys asked together.

"They catch themselves enough lightning bugs to line the hole. Then they can work by lightning bug light until they finish up."

"Honestly?" asked the boys.

"Well, that is the way it was told to me."

Then Henry couldn't keep a straight face any longer. He began to laugh. When Henry laughed, it was hard not to laugh with him. Soon the boys were giggling, too.

"We knew you were just fooling, all along."

They had reached the market house now. It was an open shed on wooden posts. Dick wanted to stop and watch for a while, but Tom was in a hurry to reach the docks.

"You can see all the ducks and chickens and garden truck you want to back home. Do hurry."

They crossed the green hillside pasture that led to Shockoe Creek. Dick stopped to rub his shoes on the grass until the mud was streaky

148

instead of solid. "That is about the best I can do, I reckon."

Several women were doing their family wash in the creek. They spread the clothes out on the grass to dry. Their children were paddling in the stream. Some of them even tried to swim where the water was deepest.

"I'd like to take a swim myself," said Dick.

"Oh, do come along."

They crossed the creek on a foot-bridge. It was almost as narrow as the cinder path. Henry was glad the boys didn't try to shove each other off the bridge.

Now, at last, they were at the river. It was a busy morning. The water was alive with batteaux, row boats, oyster boats, and sailing vessels. Some were being loaded. Some, with sails set, were already headed down stream.

Tom could have watched all day. Dick only said. "I've seen bigger ships back home."

"Come along," said Henry. "I'll show you *one* ship you don't have back home."

There was an island in the river. It was separated from the bank by only a narrow stream of water. A small vessel had been grounded there during some storm.

Now a platform led from the bank to the deck of the boat. There were tables and counters.

"Come aboard. I'll buy you some oysters."

Soon the boys were too busy eating even to say that they had bigger oysters back home. Henry had to remind them about the compromise.

THE CAPITOL

Richmond was still a new city. The Capitol was not yet finished. The Capitol Square was just a steep, weed-covered hill.

"It would take a goat to climb a hill as steep as this," Tom grumbled.

"There he is," said Henry.

The boys looked. There, sure enough, was a goat standing right on the steps. He was chewing a wisp of wild onion. Then he lowered his head. The boys thought he was coming after them. They turned and ran. Tom lost his balance. The next minute he was rolling down the hill. Dick caught at a chinquapin bush and managed to stop himself. Henry had been hunting for a stick to drive the goat away. Now he hurried to help Tom.

The goat evidently decided it wasn't worth his while to chase them. He went on chewing his wild onion. When he had swallowed the last mouthful he moved from the Capitol porch to a patch of Jamestown weed.

Tom was sitting up when Henry reached him.

"Are you hurt?" he asked anxiously.

"Shucks, no!"

It was more than could be said for his clothes. There was a hole over one knee and a tear in his sleeve. Henry straightened him up and they started up the hill again. Dick joined him.

"Our goats are smarter than that old fellow," Tom said. "They'd never have let me get away."

They entered the big hall of the Capitol.

In front of them was the Houdon statue of George Washington. They looked and looked. Even Tom was impressed.

"Mr. Houdon came over from France just to make this statue," Henry told them. "He visited in General Washington's home. He followed him around the farm. He studied him and measured him. The face is exactly like General Washington's.

"How do you know? You've never seen him."

"Yes, I have. He was in Richmond last March."

"Now," said Henry, "We'll go into the Hall of Delegates."

"Who is speaking?" asked Dick excitedly.

"We'll see." Henry was almost as eager as Dick.

Tom wasn't. He dragged along behind them. "Say, look! What is this thing?"

"A stove."

"Good lands! It's three stories high!"

"It is still a stove. I believe, though, that the man who made it called it a warming machine."

"I bet you could keep a lot warmer in front of our big fireplace back home."

"Oh, do come on!" said Dick.

At last they reached the Hall of Delegates.

"There is nothing exciting going on today," the doorkeeper told them.

Even so, Henry and Dick could have stayed there all day, looking and listening.

But Tom kept pulling at them. "Father will be waiting for us. He doesn't like to wait."

That was true. Their time was more than up. Henry and Dick pulled themselves away regretfully. They left the Capitol and started down the hill toward Mr. Denny's store.

Henry couldn't help worrying a bit as they hurried along. Even if the boys' father wasn't upset because they were late, what was he going to say when he saw their clothes? He'd probably

154

think Mr. Denny's clerk hadn't been taking very good care of his young visitors. If he was vexed, Mr. Denny would be vexed, too.

But their father only laughed when he saw them. "Well, you two look as if you've been having a pretty good time."

Henry was relieved. "But I bet their mother won't let them off that easily," he thought.

"Did you see everything?" asked Mr. Denny.

"Just about, I reckon," said Tom.

"It's a wonder," their father said. "Usually you spend most of your time quarreling."

"We compromised," said Dick. "Of course that's not so nice as having everything your own way. But Henry is right. By compromising with the other fellow you can get things done."

The Clerk's Office

THERE WAS a great deal of copying to be done in the office of the Chancery Court. It wasn't long before Mr. Tinsley sent word to Henry that there was a place for him now.

Mother was still getting ready to go to Kentucky. Henry went home for a last good-by. Mother wouldn't have a sale. George would live in the house. But it would seem terribly empty.

Even though they were busy, Polly found time to get Henry ready too.

"I'm not going to let the boy go to that court place looking like a field hand. No, indeed. I'm going to fix him up spick and span."

Starch played a large part in Polly's idea of how to make a boy look spick and span. She was going to have Henry's clothes well-starched.

Henry took a farewell trip around the plantation and to the swimming hole before he said good-by.

"It isn't forever," he told his mother. "In five or six years I'll be coming out to Kentucky too."

"But you'll be a man, not a boy, then."

"Huh!" said Polly. "That boy won't ever grow up. I caught him climbing the hickory tree yesterday. You'd better not try such didos in town unless you've got somebody to mend your britches and put starch in your clothes."

Then he was off to Richmond once more. This time there would be no coming back.

Henry had kept store long enough to know that there were various materials from which a man's clothes could be made. He hadn't earned enough money yet to buy any of them. His best

157

suit was made of good old homespun—Polly called it Figinny cloth. It was tough. It would wear. But it wasn't stylish. Besides, the suit was too loose. Even though Henry was nearly six feet tall, he was only fifteen years old. Polly had left him plenty of room to grow. And starch! His neckcloth was so stiff, he didn't dare turn his head for fear it would crack. His coattails stuck out behind as if he were making a deep bow.

The Clerk's office was in the basement of the Capitol. When he went in on the first day the room was full of young men. They were all busy writing. Every one of them stopped and stared. Some of them grinned. Henry's face was red. He wished Polly had never heard of starch.

Mr. Tinsley gave him a desk and a stool. He gave him a pen made from a goose quill. Henry sharpened his pen with his knife. He began to copy a long paper. It was almost like being in school again.

There was another boy from Hanover County in the Clerk's office.

"I am William Sharp," he told Henry. "I'll be glad to help you. So will the other boys. But they like to tease a new man at first. They may play tricks on you."

"I have two big brothers," said Henry. "I reckon I can stand to be teased."

It had been raining that day. When they left the office, the road across the Capitol Square was thick with mud.

Richmond was a very small city, but it was the only city Henry had ever seen. He liked to stop at the top of Capitol Hill and look down toward the river. He stopped to look now. One of the boys put his foot in front of him. Henry tripped. The next moment he had fallen in the mud.

The boys laughed. For a moment Henry was angry. Then he grinned too.

160

"That's one time when Hanover County Clay got mixed with Richmond City mud," he said. "Here, help me up." He held out his hand to the boy who had tripped him. Somehow, as he got up, he managed to get the boy as muddy as he was himself. They all laughed again.

"Come on," said the boy. "I know a place down by the river where we can get good oysters. We'll order supper and dry our coats in front of the fire while we eat. Then the mud will brush off."

"Maybe," hoped Henry, "some of Polly's starch will come out too."

They had a fine time in the little tavern by the river. They ate their oysters. They sang songs. They told jokes to each other.

"I'm going to like working in the Clerk's office very much," Henry thought.

The Debate Club

Henry put down his pen. He pushed back his stool. He rubbed his aching wrist.

"Copy, copy, copy, all day long," he groaned. "Why doesn't someone invent a writing machine?"

William Sharp laughed. "They tell me Mr. Thomas Jefferson is in town today. You'd better ask him to invent one for you. He's invented almost everything else."

"Have you heard about the bed he's made for himself?" one of the other boys asked. "It's between two rooms. If he gets out on one side, he is in his study. If he gets out on the other, he is in his dressing room. He has ropes to pull it up to the ceiling after he is out. Then he can walk from one room to the other."

"Here he comes down the hall now," said one of the boys near the door. The others all leaned forward to see.

"That's what I like about this place," William told Henry. "You get a chance to see and hear just about every important man in town—Patrick Henry, John Marshall, James Monroe——"

"What good does it do?" Henry asked crossly. "We never get a chance to practice."

"Practice what?" William was puzzled.

"The things we see and hear them do."

"Well, for goodness sake! Why should we?"

"You and I are going to be lawyers some day, aren't we? We want to make good speeches. It's fine to be able to hear men like Patrick Henry and John Marshall, but we ought to practice too. Did you every try to make a speech?"

William hadn't.

"Well, I have. I used to try out in the country. I made speeches to the cows and the horses. I made speeches to the cornstalks in the field. But here in the city there isn't any place where you can talk out loud to yourself. Suppose I went out in the Square and started speechmaking to the squirrels. Everyone would think I was crazy."

"That's right. But look here! Why can't we have a club? We could pay dues. Then we could rent a room in one of the taverns."

"And have orations and debates—— Say! that's a fine idea!"

THE NEW CLUB

They all agreed to get some of the boys together. But not all the boys wanted to join.

"I'd rather go see the new ropewalker at the theater," said one.

"I'm going to play billiards," said another.

But ten or twelve boys were really interested. That was enough to make a good club.

"We'll have orations at one meeting," they decided. "Then at the next we'll have a debate."

"Let's not have more than two or three speakers every night. That will leave time for us to criticize one another."

"We'll want to argue back and forth. It isn't enough to know how to make a speech you've worked up in advance. A man must learn how to think and answer quickly when he is standing in front of an audience."

"Let's draw straws to see who comes first!"

Henry didn't come first. He was glad of that. It gave him more time to get his oration ready. Oh, how he worked on that speech! It was going to be about the French Revolution.

America wasn't the only country to have a revolution. The poor people of France had been bady treated for many years. They had been fighting for their freedom for four years now. All over America people were cheering them on. This new French republic had a motto: "Liberty, Equality, Fraternity." Henry planned exactly what he wanted to say about this important motto in his speech.

He was working all day in the Clerk's office. He was writing his speech at night. But still he had time for something else. He had saved enough money now. He was going to buy a new suit of clothes.

Thomas Jefferson had just brought a new style back from France. The well-to-do men in France all wore short breeches fastened at the knee with silver or gold buckles. But the men in the poorer classes wore long trousers called pantaloons. Men who sympathized with the French Revolution also wore long trousers. Thomas Jefferson had brought back this new fashion.

Henry's new suit was going to have long pantaloons. Of course he'd wear knee breeches to parties or dances. But he could wear the new suit to make his speech.

At last the night came. He put on his new suit. He put the notes for his speech in his coattail pocket. He hurried off to his debate club.

He hadn't thought he would be nervous. Hadn't he made speeches by the dozen back home? He hadn't been nervous then. But somehow his hands grew damp and his feet twitched while he waited for his turn. He was sure it was the fire that made his face so hot. But his hands were cold.

At last the chairman called, "Mr. Clay!"

Henry wasn't used to being Mr. Clay. It made him more nervous than ever. He stood up in front of the club. "I'm not afraid," he kept telling himself. "I've made ever so many speeches before." But the cornstalks hadn't looked at him the way these boys did. The cows hadn't torn his speech to pieces the way these boys could.

"G-g-gentlemen!" Henry began. His voice wobbled. He was surprised that it could even be heard. Somehow the sound of it made him feel better. After the first few lines, it wasn't so bad. He had something he wanted to tell these boys. He wanted to make them feel about France as he felt. By the end of his speech he was almost sorry to sit down. He meant everything he had said. He had enjoyed speaking.

The boys clapped when he finished. Then they began to argue about some of the things he had said. Henry answered the arguments. It was late before the meeting broke up.

On the way out Henry heard two of the boys talking. "That was the best speech we've had."

"Yes," said the other, "he had a good subject. 'Liberty, Equality, Fraternity'—that's a mighty good motto for France or for any country."

Working for Judge Wythe

ONE OF the most interesting people who came to the Clerk's office in the Chancery Court was Judge Wythe.

When Henry first saw him, he almost laughed. The judge was such a funny-looking little old man. His head was bald. His nose looked like a bird's beak. He wore only the plainest clothes.

The boys told funny stories about him. "Folks say he takes a cold-water bath every morning." How they laughed at that!

"And he says a person's body needs a sun bath as well as a water bath. Who ever heard tell of such nonsense!"

169

"He never eats any meat."

"But he must keep strong some way because he always takes a four-mile walk every morning before breakfast."

Henry wanted to laugh when he first saw the judge. Everybody did. Once they knew him, they didn't laugh. He was a kindly old man. But the blue eyes over his hooked nose were keen and bright. He was one of the best judges in the country. He knew the law, and how to explain it.

Whenever he came into the Clerk's office the boys worked harder than ever. They weren't afraid of him exactly, but no one wanted Judge Wythe to catch him napping.

Henry had been in the Clerk's office nearly a year when Judge Wythe came in one morning. Henry's desk was near Mr. Tinsley's.

"My rheumatism is getting the best of me," said the old man. "I can't use my right hand at

170

all. I am trying to learn to write with my left hand, but it takes time. I write very slowly. I have some business that can't wait."

"What you need," said Mr. Tinsley, "is a shorthand writer. There are men, you know, who write down sounds instead of words. We had one here when the Virginia Convention met in 1788. He could take down what I said as fast as I could say it. Then he wrote it out in longhand afterwards. He didn't miss a word."

"I know," said Judge Wythe. "I saw one at the First Congress. He took down everything that was said."

Mr. Tinsley shook his head. "I don't see how they can do it."

"You'd be puzzled still more if you saw their notes. They look like a collection of pothooks."

The judge paused for a moment and then went on. "But this has nothing to do with my business. We haven't any shorthand writers here. You'll just have to lend me one of your clerks. He must be fast, of course, and write a good hand."

Mr. Tinsley looked over the room. "Young Clay is about the best clerk we have. Suppose you try him."

Henry was proud to be chosen. At the same time he was worried. Suppose he couldn't write rapidly enough. Suppose he didn't know how to spell the big words the old man would use. Well, he'd just have to do the best he could.

HARD WORK

They went to Judge Wythe's home. They went into his study. The old man sat down in a big chair by the fireplace. He had books and notes all around him. Henry sat at the desk. He sharpened his quill pen. He was ready to write. Judge Wythe spoke slowly. Sometimes he would stop and talk.

"Do you plan to study law, young man?"

"Yes, sir."

"Good! You must be honest. You must work hard. You must keep at it. Whenever I find a young man who meets these three 'musts,' I am glad to help him."

He meant what he said. Henry knew that if he could meet these three "musts," he had found a new friend.

A little later Judge Wythe stopped in the middle of a sentence. "Do you understand this?"

"Not quite," said Henry.

"Which part isn't clear?"

Henry told him. The old man explained it carefully. He went over to his shelves to find a book. "This will help you. I'll lend it to you if you wish. After you read it I'll be glad to answer any questions you have."

Henry thanked him. He put the book with his hat and greatcoat.

They went back to their work. Sometimes the old man would say, "My notes at this point are clear. You may copy them later as they stand." Or he would say, "You may write in this quotation later. I'll mark the place in this book."

They stopped for dinner. The boys had been right. There was no meat. But everything else was so good that Henry hardly noticed meat was missing.

After dinner the judge went back to the Capitol. Henry worked in the study alone. He still had to copy in the notes and the quotations. He had to get what he had written into good shape before bedtime.

He opened the book with the last quotation. Good lands! It was in Greek. No Greek had been taught in the three years Henry had spent at the old field school. He had never even seen Greek letters before. They weren't at all like the English alphabet.

"Well, I'll just have to copy it the best I can."

He'd never had such a hard piece of work in his life. His hand held the pen so tightly that his fingers ached. Even his lips hurt, he was biting them so hard.

"Those shorthand notes Mr. Tinsley was talking about couldn't look any funnier than this. But if I leave out a single wiggle, it may make the word mean something else."

At last he had finished. He stacked his papers in a tidy pile. He left them on the desk. Then he got his hat and coat and the book the judge had lent him. He took a last look at his papers. He went home.

Henry didn't sleep well that night. Suppose Judge Wythe didn't like his work. Suppose he found some mistakes in his Greek. Suppose he told Mr. Tinsley that the clerk he had borrowed was too stupid to be of any use. All the next day Henry watched the door. Every time it opened he jumped. He didn't know whether he feared or hoped that it would be the judge. But it was two days before the old man came.

When he smiled at Henry as he passed his desk, Henry felt better.

The judge and Mr. Tinsley talked about the weather for a while. They talked about the latest news from France. Then the judge said, "I wonder if you could lend me young Clay again. He did a good piece of work for me the other day. He has a keen mind."

It seemed to Henry as if the sun itself shone brighter when they walked through the Square. Even the children playing on the green looked happy. Judge Wythe liked his work!

Before he sat down at the big desk again, Henry gave the judge the book he had lent him. "Thank you very much," he said.

"Don't you want to read it?" The old man looked surprised.

"I've finished it."

"Come, come now! You couldn't have finished it so quickly."

"Yes, sir."

The old man asked him questions about it. Henry could answer all of them. Judge Wythe was much pleased.

"You have a quick mind. But be careful, young man. When a boy has a quick mind, he is apt to skim through things. He just catches the main idea. You must never do that. Be thorough. Always lay a good foundation."

"Yes, sir. I'll try."

He did try, too. But when he was in a hurry, it saved such a lot of work just to skim!

The New Lawyer

Days and weeks go by very quickly when you are having a good time. Henry felt that the next three or four years had gone almost before they started. He worked with Judge Wythe a good deal of the time. He learned to love the quiet study with its books. He learned to love the judge too.

When working hours were over, there was the debate club. He and his fellow orators had good times together. Richmond was full of young people. There were early morning rides. There was the theater. There were outdoor parties at near-by springs and dances that lasted all night.

No one could say that Henry was good-looking. His arms and legs were long and awkward. His mouth was big. The boys called him "Cotton Head." But he didn't need to be handsome to have plenty of friends. His grin was friendly. He was never embarrassed. He joked and laughed. He was always ready to help a person out. He was a very popular young man.

Sometimes he felt that he had altogether too many friends. They took too much of his time. He almost forgot that he had come to Richmond to study.

Judge Wythe didn't forget. He had taught a good many boys in his lifetime. He had seen them grow into useful men. They had become the leaders of their country. He had taught John Marshall. He had taught Thomas Jefferson.

"It is a fine thing to be a teacher," he told Henry. "Then you may be sure that your ideas will live long after you are gone."

Now he was teaching Henry. They didn't have a special hour for lessons. He would explain things while they were working. He would tell Henry what to study. He would lend him books.

Judge Wythe kept an eye on how time was passing. He kept an eye on Henry's good times too. Henry learned to love the old man.

Finally there came an afternoon when they had finished work. He leaned back in his chair.

"Clay, I want to talk with you."

Henry wondered if he had made some big mistake in his copying.

"You're nineteen now. If you're going to be a lawyer, it is time for you to buckle down. You must begin to study law in earnest.

"I hate to lose a good secretary, but there is an opening in Attorney General Brooke's office. You can study law under him. I have said a good word for you. He said to send you over this afternoon to talk with him."

Of course, Henry was pleased and excited. Any young man who had a chance to study under Mr. Brooke was lucky. But he looked around the comfortable study. The firelight shone on the wall.

"I'll hate to leave this place."

"You can come back to see us," said the judge. "We shall welcome you back, the old room and I, whenever you come."

Outside the air was cold and sparkling. The wind was blowing the last leaves from the sweet gum trees in the Square. Henry walked briskly. His new yellow top boots shone. The nearer he came to Mr. Brooke's office, the more excited he felt. Judge Wythe had recommended him. He had given Henry the chance.

The next winter was one of the busiest that Henry had ever known. He studied law in Mr. Brooke's office. He lived in Mr. Brooke's home. There wasn't a minute that wasn't filled. In the daytime he read heavy books of law. He wrote out long pages of notes. At night in his room he studied. Of course it was hard work. But Henry was interested in law. The more he studied it, the more he liked it. In less than a year he was ready for his examination.

"I hate examinations," said one of the boys.

Henry grinned. "Remember how Robin Hood's men got tired of just practicing with their bows and arrows? Getting ready for an archery contest was much more interesting."

"Studying for an examination is interesting?"

"Well, examinations give me a chance to prove to myself whether I really know a thing."

"Enjoy your chance to prove it tomorrow."

"I don't know as I'll go that far." Henry was nervous and a little frightened. But the examination was exciting. He passed it. In November, 1797, he received his license to practice law in Virginia. He had become a lawyer.

Good-by!

"WHAT WILL you do now?" asked the judge. "Will you settle down here in Richmond?"

Young Lawyer Henry Clay shook his head. "I haven't seen my mother for five years. I reckon a lawyer can earn his living in Kentucky."

Judge Wythe chuckled. "I wouldn't be surprised. When will you go?"

"Oh, it won't take me long to get ready. I suppose I'll have to wait until my washerwoman can put some extra starch in my shirts. I can't let old Polly think I've been a disgrace to the family. But it won't take me long to pack. I can get everything I own into my saddlebags."

184

"It won't take long to pack," agreed the judge, "but it may take a while to say good-by."

That was true. Henry remembered the first day he came to Richmond. He didn't know a soul then. Now he had to stop and speak to nearly everybody he met.

He went to Mr. Denny's store. He said good-by to his friends there. He went to Mr. Tinsley's office. He said good-by to his friends there. He went to Mr. Brooke's office. He said good-by to his friends there. Then there were ever so many other good-by calls to pay. Older men, older women, young men, girls—Henry had made friends with everybody.

The debating club held a special good-by meeting for him. Henry made a farewell speech.

Finally his good-bys were said. His saddlebags were packed. Early the next morning his horse was brought around to the door. Some of his friends had come to say "Good-by" again.

Henry rode out to the end of Broad Street. He turned into Brook Road. For the first mile or so he felt very sad.

"Whenever I make friends, I have to leave them," he thought. "Life is so full of good-bys."

But the sun was shining. The skies were blue. The air was snappy and brisk. Henry began to feel happier. He remembered that at last he was going to see the mountains. He was going to see Little Sam and Jim again. Why, they were young men by now! He was going to see Mr. Watkins and Aunt Mary and Uncle John and his brothers and sisters. Best of all, he was going to see his Mother. His heart beat faster.

The sun had gone behind a cloud for a minute. Now it was shining out again.

Henry was on a long stretch of open road.

"Hurrah!" he cried to his horse. "Let's gallop for the fun of galloping. We're off to Kentucky! We're really off to Kentucky!"

Henry Clay, Patriot

This is the story of the boy Henry Clay. It ends when he went to Kentucky. But there are always questions at the end of a story. Did Henry like Kentucky?

He did. The people of Kentucky liked him too. First they elected him to their State Legislature. Later they sent him to Congress in Washington. There he became one of the outstanding men in American history.

It wasn't because he was always able to get things done the way he wanted them. People often voted against him and his ideas. Three times he tried to become President. Three times he was defeated. "I'd rather be right than President," he said. He fought hard for the things in which he believed. Then if he failed, he was a good loser. He was never bitter.

"Where did I make my mistake?" he would ask himself. Then he would try again.

He helped the United States grow from a feeble new republic into a strong nation. Patrick Henry once said, "I am not a Virginian but an American." Henry felt the same way. "I know no North, no South, no East, no West."

When it looked as if war were coming, he did all that he could to keep peace.

There came a cold day in February 1850. Henry was an old man now. He was ill too.

"You aren't strong enough to go to the Capitol today," said his Washington friends.

He laughed at them. "I must. The North and the South are ready to fight each other. Our Union will be broken up. I am an old man. May-

189

be they will listen to me. Maybe I can make them see how foolish they are. If each side will give in just a little! If only they will compromise!"

He was so weak he had to be helped up the Capitol steps. As if to make up for the cold outside, the Senate chamber was overheated. It was packed with excited people. The windows were closed. The air was close and stifling. It was no place for a sick man. But Henry Clay was determined to do his best to save his country. He might be an old man but he made one of the best speeches of his whole life.

He begged the people to forget their differences and to remember their country.

He spoke for three hours. The next day he was ready to start all over again. All through the winter and spring he worked for the laws which he felt would keep his country from war.

Summer came. With the hot weather some of the senators wanted to take a little rest.

"No," said Clay, "not until we have decided this question."

At last it was decided. The North gave in a little. The South gave in a little. There was no war as long as Henry Clay was alive.

He had been the Speaker of the House of Representatives three times. He had been a senator four times. He had been Secretary of State. He filled these offices well. But we remember him, not for these things, but because he believed so strongly in our United States. He is remembered because he tried to keep the states at peace.

Sometimes he was called the peacemaker, the "Great Pacificator." "Let each side give in a little. Then we can work together for the good of the whole country."

That is why we still call him one of the great men of America. He loved his country. He worked to make it a better country. He was a true patriot.

More About This Book

WHEN HENRY CLAY LIVED

1777   HENRY CLAY WAS BORN IN HANOVER COUNTY, VIRGINIA, APRIL 12.

The thirteen English colonies had declared their independence from Great Britain.

1777–
1797   HENRY GREW UP ON THE FARM, WORKED IN RICHMOND, AND STUDIED LAW.

The peace treaty with England was signed, ending the Revolutionary War, 1783.

The Constitutional Convention met to frame the United States Constitution, 1787.

George Washington was President, 1789-1797.

1797–
1803   CLAY PRACTICED LAW IN KENTUCKY.

John Adams was President, 1797-1801.

Thomas Jefferson was President, 1801-1809.

Washington became the new capital of the United States, 1800.

1803–
1811   CLAY SERVED AS A KENTUCKY LEGISLATOR AND AS A UNITED STATES SENATOR.

The United States bought the Louisiana Territory from France, 1803.

Lewis and Clark explored the Northwest, 1804-1806.

Robert Fulton built the "Clermont," first practical steamboat, 1807.

1811–
1831   CLAY SERVED AS A UNITED STATES REPRESENTATIVE AND AS SECRETARY OF STATE.

The War of 1812 was fought, 1812-1815.

Florida was purchased from Spain, 1819.

The Erie Canal was completed, 1825.

1831–
1852   CLAY SERVED SEVERAL TERMS AS A UNITED STATES SENATOR.

Cyrus McCormick invented the reaper, 1831.

Samuel Morse invented the telegraph, 1835.

American settlers reached Oregon, 1836.

The Mexican War was fought, 1846-1848.

The Compromise of 1850, sponsored by Henry Clay, was passed.

1852 HENRY CLAY DIED, JUNE 29.

There were thirty-one states in the Union.

Millard Fillmore was President.

The population of the country was about 24,000,000.

DO YOU REMEMBER?

1. How were people baptized, according to the opening story in the book?

2. Why did Henry have to eat at the second table during the company dinner?

3. What exciting news did Aaron and Henry hear at Hanover Court House?

4. How did the British soldiers mistreat the Clay family when they came to the house?

5. How did Aaron and Henry feed the American soldiers across the swollen stream?

6. How did Henry and his family learn that Cornwallis had surrendered?

7. What game about Indians and settlers did Henry play with the other children?

8. Where did Aunt Mary and her family decide to go to live?

9. How did Henry happen to hear Patrick Henry make a speech?

10. Why did Henry come to be called the Mill Boy of the Slashes?

11. What job did Henry get when he and Mr. Walters went to Richmond?

12. How did Henry help to form a debating club while working in the Hanover County clerk's office?

13. How did Henry get an opportunity to work for and study law with Judge Wythe?

14. Where did young Henry Clay go to live after he became a lawyer?

15. What different government offices did Clay hold after he moved to Kentucky?

16. Why was he called the "Great Pacificator"?

IT'S FUN TO LOOK UP THESE THINGS

1. Where is Hanover County, in which Henry Clay was born?

2. What important war was being fought when Henry Clay was born?

3. How did young men prepare to become lawyers in Henry Clay's time?

4. Why did many people move westward from Virginia to Kentucky and Tennessee in the early days of our country?

5. What are the duties of the speaker of the United States House of Representatives?

6. Who was President of the United States when Clay was Secretary of State?

INTERESTING THINGS YOU CAN DO

1. Draw a map to show where Henry Clay lived in Kentucky.

2. Read to find out how Clay traveled between his home and Washington, D. C.

3. Make a list of other statesmen who lived at the same time as Clay.

4. Find out when Clay ran for President of the United States.

5. Prepare a report on the Whig political party to which Clay belonged.

6. Collect pictures of Clay for an exhibit on the bulletin board.

OTHER BOOKS YOU MAY ENJOY READING

Champions of Peace, Edith Patterson Meyer. Little.

Dan Webster: Union Boy, Bradford Smith. Trade and School Editions, Bobbs-Merrill.

Fight for the Union, The, Margaret Coit. Houghton.

Henry Clay: Statesman and Patriot, Regina Z. Kelly. Houghton.

Patrick, Son of Thunder: A Biography of Patrick Henry, D. M. Stephenson. Reilly & Lee.

Profiles in Courage, John F. Kennedy. Harper.

INTERESTING WORDS IN THIS BOOK

argue (är′gū) : offer reasons for or against something

audience (ô′dĭ ĕns) : people gathered together to hear a speaker

batteaux (bă tōz′) : light, flat-bottomed boats tapering toward both ends

beeswax (bēz′wăks′) : honeycomb

capital (kăp′ĭ tăl) : city where the government of a country or state is located

chaise (shāz) : two-wheeled covered carriage, pulled by one horse

compromise (kŏm′prō mīz) : arbitrate, settle or decide something by making concessions

Constitution (kŏn′stĭ tū shŭn) : document adopted for governing our country

debate (dĕ bāt′) : public argument for and against a question

delegate (dĕl′ĕ gȧt) : person who represents others

despise (dĕ spīz′) : look down upon, scorn

disappoint (dĭs′ȧ point′) : upset hopes or plans

embarrass (ĕm băr′ăs) : make a person appear to blame for something

fraternity (frȧ tûr′nĭ tĭ) : organization of men or boys for business, social, or religious purposes

furrow (fûr′ō) : long trench in a field or garden cut by a plow

governor (gŭv′ĕr nĕr) : person elected to the highest office in a state of the United States

huddle (hŭd″l) : crowd together

impress (ĭm prĕs′) : affect strongly and favorably

interrupt (ĭn′tĕ rŭpt′) : break in on a conversation or a speech

lawyer (lô′yẽr) : trained person who gives advice about legal matters and represents other persons in court

legislature (lĕj′ĭs lā′tŭr) : group of persons elected by a state or country to make laws

motto (mŏt′ō) : word or expression used as a maxim or rule of conduct

munch (mŭnch) : chew noisily

opportunity (ŏp′ŏr tū′nĭ tĭ) : good chance

peculiar (pė̇ kūl′yẽr) : unusual, different

plantation (plăn tā′shŭn) : large tract of land cultivated by laborers

quotation (kwȯ̇ tā′shŭn) : words of one person written or spoken exactly by another person

rampaging (răm pāj′ĭng) : storming or rushing about wildly

rheumatism (rōō′mȧ tĭz′m) : disease which causes swelling and stiffness of the joints

scurry (skûr′ĭ) : hurry

smokehouse (smōk′hous′) : small building where meat or fish is cured in dense smoke

surrender (sŭ̇ rĕn′dẽr) : give up

victuals (vĭt′l′z) : food

200